A Workbook for Dyslexics

A Complete Reading Program for Struggling Readers and Those with Dyslexia

Third Edition

Cheryl Orlassino

**Reading Specialists
of Long Island**

Creative
Dragon Press

Visit our product site at
www.YourKidCanRead.com

* Bulk Rate Discounts Available *

Our other reading programs:
I Can Read - Book A
I Can Read - Book B
Blast Off to Reading!

Published By Creative Dragon Press
Centereach, New York

e-mail all inquiries to:
dyslexia.help@YourKidCanRead.com

Printed in the United States of America
Third Edition - Rev A
International Standard Book Number (ISBN): 978-0-9831996-6-3

Table of Contents

Reading Program Instructions

Work every day at the student's pace for 45-60 minutes. Each lesson usually contains a new topic, a review (lists of words and sentences) and then exercises. **Italicized text is meant for you, the instructor, to read to yourself.** When you come upon letters inside of slashes, that is meant for you to say the actual *sound* of the letter. Anything in single quotes is meant for you to **spell** out.

Example: If you see /ar/ (in slashes), you would read it as the sound "ar" (as in "jar").
If you see 'ar' (in single quotes), you would read it as the letters "a", "r".

A lesson is not meant to be done in one sitting, although that can happen. Don't rush your student; let him/ her do this program at his/her own pace. The first few lessons may seem very easy for the student and possibly insulting, but **do not skip them;** they are extremely important for providing a good foundation for phoneme awareness. If your student feels insulted, show him/her the larger words at the end of the book and explain how you have to provide a good foundation to read those words.

Do *every* lesson and exercise with your student (except for the dictations, which will be discussed below) - **they cannot do this on their own**.

Dictations

Most lessons require that the student write words and sentences in a "dictation book". For this, a composition book dedicated for this purpose is recommended. Date the page at the top so you can see how improvement progresses over time.

   On-line dictations are available at: www.yourkidcanread.com. **A PDF with the word lists will also be available for you to print out (which you will need to check the work).**

Each dictation should be done until you feel it has been mastered (note that in later lessons, you can be more lax, since the words are more difficult and reading them is our primary goal at this point). **If a dictation is not mastered, continue moving forward with the lessons**, however take time to redo old, un-mastered dictations each day before you start a lesson or continue a lesson that has not been completed. If the student has not mastered the dictation, simply record the score, correct it **with the student** and move on. If you find yourself with a backlog of un-mastered dictations, you may need to stop moving forward and review older lessons until you are caught up.

Do not let the student study and memorize the words (unless otherwise noted). He/she should use the sounds and rules learned to figure out the spelling. When done, correct the work with your student. Have him/her **read the words to you from their own handwriting** and write the corrected word next to any that were misspelled, making sure to use the rules learned. There is no need to write the misspelled word over many times. ***Have your student say the letter sounds out loud as he or she writes them, not the letter names.***

For the sentences: make sure the student leaves a line or two between the sentences so there is room for the corrections. When checking, have your student read the sentences to you from their own writing (as done for the words). If a word is misspelled, have him/her sound it out and try to correct it. Help when needed. Note that sometimes the student may omit entire words, switch words around or even change a word. This is very common. All corrections should be made on the lines above or below the sentences.

If a letter is reversed, but all else is correct, simply have your student write over the letter and count the word as correct (keep a note of the reversals so you can address them later).

Flash Cards

Most lessons introduce new sounds or rules that will need constant review before each lesson, which is done using flash cards. You can either make your own cards or purchase them ready-made, or a PDF version, at www.YourKidCanRead.com. To create your own cards, write the new rule or sound that is introduced on the card using a bold marker. If, for example, the sound is 'nk', write "ank, enk, ink, onk, unk" on *one* card. If there is any rule, memory trick, or word that you feel your student should memorize, put it on a flash card.

If you purchased the flash cards, add the card to the "review pile" only after the sound or rule is covered in the lesson. **Test the student every day before each lesson using these cards.** Once a sound or rule is completely mastered, you can remove the card from the pile.

> * Some lessons contain words that do not follow normal phonics rules. You may want to write these words on index cards and add them to your flash card pile for reinforcement.

Important Tips

In the beginning, depending on the severity of the reading problem, you may need to spend some extra time developing phoneme awareness (connecting the smallest units of sounds together). You can use lowercase letter tiles, magnetic letters or a white board to create sounds, as done in the first three lessons. ***Always use lowercase since this is what most words are comprised of.***

A typical lesson is as follows:
1. Go through the flash cards for the sounds & rules.
2. Redo dictations that were not mastered.
3. Continue with the lesson (you may be starting a new lesson or continuing a lesson that has not been completed).

In addition to this book, you will need:
1. Lowercase letter tiles or plastic alphabet magnets (optional)
2. A white board – this is highly recommended since you can illustrate the material that is covered in an interactive manner.
3. A composition notebook (for the dictations)
4. Index cards (or flash cards, available at www.yourkidcanread.com)
5. Access to the internet for on-line dictations.

➢ Since many letter names are different from their actual sounds (such as 'w' – 'double-u'), instruct your student to say (out loud) **the letter sounds as he or she writes, not the letter names**. If *you* are decoding a word to the student, **never** say the actual letter names, only say the sounds. Letter names should only be used when introducing a new sound which is comprised of two or more letters, such as the /th/ sound. However, once the sound is introduced, when you see those letters in a word, you should only say the actual *sound*.

➢ When a student has trouble reading a word, cover it up with your finger and slowly reveal the letters. If the letter needs another letter to make a sound (such as 'th') then reveal both letters at one time. This will force the student to decode left to right, taking each sound at a time.

thin
th
thi
thin

➢ If you see your student becoming frustrated, then slow down and review something else. You don't want to give too much at one time.

➢ When you reach lesson 19, long vowels, your student should begin reading books out loud to you for five to ten minutes a day. When he or she has trouble decoding a word, help out using the above method (cover the word with your finger). For words that have sounds or rules that were not yet covered, you should read that word to him/her only if needed. Eventually, he/she should start reading on his/her own. The more books read, the better reader and writer they will become.

Part 1 – Assessing Consonant Sounds
Have your student read the consonant sounds to you.
You will need to work on sounds that were incorrectly read.

Note that 'c' and 'g' should be hard sounds as in "cat" and "get", and 'y' should have the sound as in "yellow".

b ___	h ___	n ___	v ___
c ___	j ___	p ___	w ___
d ___	k ___	r ___	x ___
f ___	l ___	s ___	y ___
g ___	m ___	t ___	z ___

Read the following to your student:

'x' makes the /ks/ sound
as in "fox" and "box".

Exercise 1.1
Read the following words to your student and have him/her write the beginning consonant sounds in his/her notebook:

1. van	4. yellow	7. nest	10. jump	13. man	16. rain
2. zoo	5. bear	8. sun	11. top	14. pig	17. wall
3. hat	6. fan	9. lamp	12. duck	15. game	

*Before continuing, you should work on any consonant sounds that were not correctly identified.

Part 2- Vowels
Vowels are special letters that have more than one sound. They have a short sound and a long sound. The long sound is simply their name. For example, the long 'a' sound is 'a'. However, the long vowel sound for 'u' is sometimes /oo/ as in "boo".

A Workbook for Dyslexics - Cheryl Orlassino -8-

The Vowels
a e i o u

Part 3- Short Vowels

Short vowels have special sounds that you must memorize.
To do this, we associate each sound with a particular
picture that starts with that sound.
If you are reading a word and aren't sure which short vowel
sound to use, match the letter up with the picture
that starts with the same letter.

short 'a' -   /ah/ apple

short 'e' -   /eh/ elephant

short 'i' -   /ih/ igloo

short 'o'-   /oh/ octopus

short 'u' -   /uh/ umbrella

*Whenever your student has trouble with a short vowel sound,
you should say the picture name associated with that vowel,
emphasizing the beginning sound.*

Exercise 1.2

*Point to each picture and ask your student to say the beginning
short vowel sound and picture name (such as "/eh/ - elephant"):*

Exercise 1.3
Circle the vowels:

a b c d e f g h I j k l m n o p q r s t u v w x y z

Exercise 1.4
*Have the your say the short vowel sounds for the following,
(go down each column):*

a	e	i	o	i
u	i	e	e	a
e	o	a	i	u
o	u	i	a	e
i	a	o	u	o

Exercise 1.5
*Read the following words to your student and have him/her
identify whether the vowel sound is long or short:*

1.	pin	long	short
2.	pine	long	short
3.	can	long	short
4.	cane	long	short
5.	ripe	long	short
6.	rip	long	short

short, long, short, long, long, short

Exercise 1.6
*Read the words below to your student and have him/her write in
his/her notebook the beginning short vowel sounds:*

1. ever	5. opposite	9. impossible	13. upper
2. actor	6. exit	10. after	14. issue
3. October	7. under	11. odd	15. invitation
4. India	8. obvious	12. enable	16. obnoxious

Consonant-Vowel Combinations

In this lesson, we are going to read short vowels with consonants,
but first lets review our short vowel sounds.
Say the short vowel sound for the pictures below:

Say the short vowel sound for the letters below:

a	e	i	o	i
u	i	e	e	a
e	o	a	i	u
o	u	i	a	e
i	a	o	u	o

'x' makes what sound? _____

Now we're going to put vowels and consonants together.
When you read these, all 'c's should be hard /k/ sounds,
as in the word "cat", and all 'g's should be hard sounds
as in the word "get". Now try reading the following:

ga   bi   tu   ac   ob   et

Have your student read the letter combinations below:
All vowels are short (so the words like "go" or "we" are *not* words,
they only have short vowel sounds, such as /goh/ and /weh/).
Remember, 'g' and 'c' are hard sounds, as in "get" and "cat".

CV - Consonant / Vowel Sounds:

pa	da	ca	ga	ma	na	ba
ka	la	fa	ja	sa	ta	va
wa	ra	ta	ha	za	da	ya
pe	de		ge	me	ne	be
ke	le	fe	je	se	te	ve
we	re	te	he	ze	de	ye
pi	di		gi	mi	ni	bi
ki	li	fi	ji	si	ti	vi
wi	ri	ti	hi	zi	di	yi
po	do	co	go	mo	no	bo
ko	lo	fo	jo	so	to	vo
wo	ro	to	ho	zo	do	yo
pu	du	cu	gu	mu	nu	bu
ku	lu	fu	ju	su	tu	vu
wu	ru	tu	hu	zu	du	yu

Remember, 'c' and 'g' are hard sounds as in "cat" and "get".

VC - Vowel / Consonant Sounds:

ap	ad	ac	ag	am	an	ab
ak	al	af	aj	as	at	av
ax	ap	at	ax	az	ad	ah
ep	ed	ec	eg	em	en	eb
ek	el	ef	ej	es	et	ev
ex	ep	et	ex	ez	ed	eh
ip	id	ic	ig	im	in	ib
ik	il	if	ij	is	it	iv
ix	ip	it	ix	iz	id	ih
op	od	oc	og	om	on	ob
ok	ol	of	oj	os	ot	ov
ox	op	ot	ox	oz	od	oh
up	ud	uc	ug	um	un	ub
uk	ul	uf	uj	us	ut	uv
ux	up	ut	ux	uz	ud	uh

The following are high frequency words that are not spelled the way they sound. See which words your student can read. Put these on flash cards and review until mastered.

the	you	his	of	she	was
me	to	is	has	we	said
my	do	he	have	they	does

Many of the words listed above do not sound the way they are spelled.
In the next exercise, we will look at these words and their sounds.
Note that the slashes mean "sound of":

Example: /f/ = the 'f' sound as in "fast"

Exercise 2.1

Draw lines to match the sound of the underlined letters to the sounds on the right (which may be used more than once):

1. m<u>y</u>

2. m<u>e</u>

3. o<u>f</u>

4. wa<u>s</u>

5. doe<u>s</u>

6. i<u>s</u>

7. h<u>e</u>

8. hi<u>s</u>

9. sh<u>e</u>

10. th<u>ey</u>

  'a'

  'e'

  'i'

  /v/

  /z/

1. 'ī'
2. 'ē'
3. /v/
4. /z/
5. /z/
6. /z/
7. 'ē'
8. /z/
9. 'ē'
10. 'ā'

Exercise 2.2
Circle the words that have the /oo/, as in "boo", sound (there are 3):

the	his	of	me	does	she
is	to	has	do	said	we
he	my	have	they	was	you

to, do, you

Exercise 2.3
Read the following to the student and have him or her circle the answer:

1. The 'e' in "me" makes what sound?

   long 'e'   short 'i'   short 'e'

2. The 'ey' in "they" makes what sound?

   long 'a'   short 'a'   short 'e'

3. The 'e' in "he" makes what sound?

   long 'a'   short 'i'   long 'e'

4. The 'y' in "my" makes what sound?

   long 'i'   short 'i'   long 'e'

long 'e', long 'a', long 'e', long 'i'

Exercise 2.4
Read the following to the student, omitting the word choices, and have him/ her circle the word that makes sense:

1. **My / You** house is just around the corner.

2. I **is / was** going to leave early today.

3. Brian **have / has** enough money to buy the car.

4. The man thought **he / you** were talking to him.

5. **He / They** are going to the game on Saturday.

6. He **is / was** driving last night when he got stuck.

My, was, has, you, They, was

Exercise 2.5

Read the words to your student and have him/her tell you if the vowel sound is long or short:

1.	robe	long / short		7.	kit	long / short
2.	rob	long / short		8.	kite	long / short
3.	tap	long / short		9.	spite	long / short
4.	tape	long / short		10.	spit	long / short
5.	fine	long / short		11.	shin	long / short
6.	fin	long / short		12.	shine	long / short

1) long, 2) short, 3) short, 4) long, 5) long, 6) short,
7) short, 8) long, 9) long, 10) short, 11) short, 12) long

Exercise 2.6

Read the following sentences to your student and have him/her fill in the blank with the word that makes sense (some words may be interchangeable):

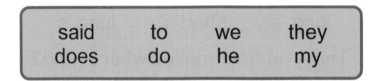

said	to	we	they
does	do	he	my

1. What time does _____ have to get up?

2. She _____ not have enough time to shop.

3. They have a lot of work to _____ .

4. Jim was driving out _____ the beach.

5. The professor _____ that we have to show our work.

6. _____ have all seen the movie.

7. _____ were going to go fishing on the lake.

8. I let Tim borrow _____ ladder.

In the last lesson, you put together sounds made up from vowels and consonants. In this lesson, we are going to read simple three letter words, where the middle vowel has a short sound.

If you have trouble identifying a **short vowel** sound, think of the pictures below:

a -   e -   i -   o -   u -

Read the word below (note that some are nonsense words):

pad	gad	bad	fat	tat	pap	zab
dad	mad	tap	jab	vat	taz	daf
cad	nad	lap	sat	tax	max	pan
pet	jeb	bed	fet	ted	pep	zet
ded	met	tep	jet	vet	ten	deb
ked	net	lep	set	tex	mex	pen
pin	jig	bib	fit	tig	pip	zit
did	mit	kin	jim	vib	tip	dig
kid	nit	lip	sit	tix	mix	pit
pop	got	bob	fot	top	pog	zop
dod	mos	con	job	vob	tob	dog
cos	nop	lop	sot	nox	mox	pot
put	gut	bub	fub	tum	pub	zun
dud	mus	kut	jut	vut	tub	dub
cub	num	lup	sut	nux	mux	pup

Read the following:

1. The cat was on the mat.
2. The pot was hot.
3. The dog is a mutt.
4. The pig is in the box.
5. The fan is on.
6. Put the map in the van.

Exercise 3.1

Identify and write the short vowel which is in the middle of the words for the pictures below:

1.	7.	13.
2.	8.	14.
3.	9.	15.
4.	10.	16.
5.	11.	17.
6.	12.	18.

1) u, 2) a, 3) o, 4) a, 5) u, 6) i, 7) a, 8) u, 9) a, 10) o, 11) i, 12) o 13) u, 14) a, 15) o, 16) i, 17) a, 18) o

Exercise 3.2

Read the following to your student (use the word "blank" for the unfinished words) and have him/her fill in the missing consonant:

1. I fell and hurt my _____**eg.**
2. He got **ma**_____ at the boy.
3. The dog _____**it** my leg.
4. I took a **si**_____ of the drink.
5. Get **ri**_____ of the trash.
6. I wore **ca**_____ on my head.
7. The sun is very **ho**_____.
8. The sports car is **re**_____.

leg, mad, bit, sip, rid, cap, hot, red

Exercise 3.3
Have the student fill in a missing vowel to make a real word (don't allow repeat words):

1. h___t	5. p___t	9. s___n
2. p___n	6. w___n	10. b___x
3. h___g	7. t___p	11. n___p
4. m___n	8. s___p	12. f___x

Answers will vary.

Exercise 3.4
*Have **your student** read the sentences and circle the word that makes sense:*

1. My cat sits on my **lap / lip**.

5. My pet is at the **vet / sun**.

2. His dad is a lot of **fan / fun**.

6. The pen is in the **can / nut**.

3. The pig is in the **cup / mud**.

7. His dad has a big **tan / dog**.

4. It was his cat on the **hat / mat**.

8. Is a rat in the **box / fan** ?

Exercise 3.5
Read the sentences to your student, omitting the word choices, and have him/her circle the word that makes sense:

1. Where did **we / my** wallet go?

2. **They / She** have been waiting in line a long time.

3. He **have / has** a baseball game tonight.

4. My girlfriend **was / does** not like spiders.

5. Tom **was / is** at my house yesterday.

Exercise 3.6
Do the dictations for this lesson at www.yourkidcanread.com.

Consonant Blends

In this lesson, we have **two or more** consonants that are together so that their sounds blend into each other.
*Read the following sounds to the student,
and then have him/her read them back:*

Beginning Blends:

st	br	sn	cl	tr	bl	cr
fl	gr	sc	sp	sm	sl	pl
dr	pr	sw	tw	gl	fr	sk
		str	scr	spl		

Read the following:

stop	clot	cram	scab	slam	prob	glad
brit	trap	flit	spat	plot	swim	grub
snag	blot	grab	smit	drat	twin	flat
		strap	scrap	split		

Exercise 4.1

Write the consonant blends for the <u>beginning</u> sounds for the following pictures:

1. _____ _____

2. _____ _____

3. _____ _____

4. _____ _____

5. _____ _____

6. _____ _____

7. _____ _____

8. _____ _____

9. _____ _____

stamp, flat, clock, plant, broom, trap, drip, swim, tree

Consonant blends can also happen at the end of a word (or in the middle). Below are the common ending consonant blends:

Ending Blends:

st	mp	sp	sm	ld	ft	lt
lk	lf	lm	lp	nt	pt	sk

Read the following:

fa**st**	he**ld**	mi**lk**	fi**lm**	a**sk**
lu**mp**	le**ft**	si**lk**	he**lp**	ke**pt**
ga**sp**	wi**lt**	se**lf**	we**nt**	ta**sk**

Exercise 4.2

Write the consonant blends for the <u>ending</u> sounds for the following pictures:

1. ___ ___

3. ___ ___

5. ___ ___

2. ___ ___

4. ___ ___

6. ___ ___

lamp, belt, list, stump, plant, milk

Have the student read the following going across:

rap - flap - trap	rip - strip - strap
tip - trip - slip	lip - clip - flip
bet - belt - bent	trap - tramp - trump
lap - lamp - limp	spit - split - spilt
sap - slap - snap	plan - plant - pant
lit - list - lost	rant - grant - grunt
bat - brat - brag	bump - jump - stump
pat - pant - plant	list - lost - cost

-21-

Exercise 4.3
Fill in the missing vowel to make a real word:

a   e   i   o   u

1. h___lp   5. cl___p   9. dr___p

2. pl___n   6. st___p   10. sp___t

3. cr___m   7. tr___p   11. sk___p

4. st___p   8. pl___g   12. spl___t

Answers will vary.

Exercise 4.4
Read the following sentences to your student and have him/her fill in the blank with a word from the list.

Make sure you say the letter **sounds** out loud as you write (NOT the letter names):

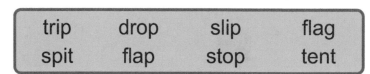

| trip | drop | slip | flag |
| spit | flap | stop | tent |

1. If you walk on ice, you may _____ and fall.

2. When driving, a red light means you should _____ .

3. It is not polite to _____ in public.

4. This summer we are going on a _____ to the beach.

5. A bird has to _____ its wings to fly.

6. On the fourth of July, we display our _____ .

7. If you catch on fire, you should stop, _____ and roll.

8. When you go camping, you pitch a _____ .

Exercise 4.5
Circle the sound to make a real word (there is one per line):

1. fl____   ot   op   ad

2. dr____   ag   in   am

3. gr____   op   ot   ab

4. dr____   op   ot   ig

5. tr____   ag   ab   ot

6. tr____   ap   on   ag

7. tr____   ut   en   ip

8. sp____   ut   in   ip

9. sp____   ag   ig   an

10. spl____   it   ot   ut

split
span
spin
trip
trot
drop
grab
drag
flop

Exercise 4.6
Draw a line to match the sounds to make as many real words as possible (sounds on the right may be used more than once):

1. mi____

2. be__

3. si__

4. fa__

5. ve__

6. li__

lt

lk

st

mp

limp
list
vest
fast
silk
silt
best
belt
mist
milk

Exercise 4.7
Do the dictations for this lesson at www.yourkidcanread.com.

-23-

Lesson 5
The /ch/ and /sh/ Sounds

Words are made up of letters that make sounds. Sometimes the word is only a few letters long, and you can sound out each letter and put the word together. Sometimes, certain groups, or pairs, of letters make up certain sounds that we have to remember. In this lesson, we will look at 'ch' and 'sh', which both make special sounds that we must know when we see them in a word.

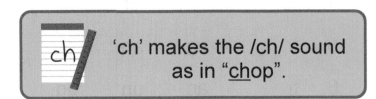

'ch' makes the /ch/ sound as in "<u>ch</u>op".

<u>ch</u>op   <u>ch</u>amp   <u>ch</u>ip   <u>ch</u>ap   ri<u>ch</u>

*Note that 'ch' usually makes the /ch/ sound (as in "chop"), but it also can be a /k/ sound as in "chord" or a /sh/ sound as in "chef". More often than not, when you see a 'ch' it will be the /ch/ sound, as in the above words. We will see the other sounds toward the end of this book.

Read the following:

belch	chat	chip	much
champ	chimp	chop	rich
chap	chin	chug	such

Spelling Rule: Add a 't' before the 'ch':

When 'ch' is next to a **short** vowel, a 't' *usually* needs to be added to separate the vowel from the 'ch'.

hi<u>t</u>**ch**   swi<u>t</u>**ch**   ca<u>t</u>**ch**   ma<u>t</u>**ch**   ki<u>t</u>**ch**en

Some exceptions: much, rich, touch, such, and which

-24-

*Read the following to the student and then
have him or her read them back (all vowels are short):*

atch   etch   itch   otch   utch

*Remember to put new sounds or rules on index cards and have
your student read them every day until they are mastered.*

Read the following; notice how you don't hear the 't':

catch	fetch	hutch	patch	stitch
clutch	hatch	itch	pitch	switch
etch	hitch	match	scratch	witch

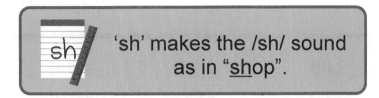

'sh' makes the /sh/ sound
as in "<u>sh</u>op".

<u>sh</u>op   <u>sh</u>ip   <u>sh</u>am   <u>sh</u>rug   di<u>sh</u>

*Read the following to the student and then
have him or her read them back (all vowels are short):*

ash   esh   ish   osh   ush

Read the following:

crash	gash	shop	shrimp	wish	plush
bash	crush	ship	flush	fish	dish
trash	shut	rush	shag	mesh	sash

Review:

pa	te	mi	wu	at	ip	bo
ab	ta	tu	ca	ag	ib	pu
bi	bo	wi	po	aj	id	mi

ba	cu	pi	ot	um	am	ib
bat	cut	pin	got	bum	ham	rib
ca	pa	it	ut	im	ub	in
cab	pan	bit	hut	dim	tub	win

tut	rug	mut	sat	pot	dab	den
tot	mat	rat	pig	bun	sag	nap
rig	mit	rot	pog	ban	nod	pan
rag	mot	sit	pat	nip	pit	pun

---

blip	crip	grip	spun	tram
bust	crot	grin	smut	tramp
brap	crud	plan	snag	trap
crab	drag	plot	snug	trim
crat	flab	plum	swat	trip
crib	glad	scrap	swit	trot

---

blush	smash	shut	shot	hutch
brush	sham	shin	mash	switch
crash	ship	swish	snatch	rich
crush	shrimp	hush	patch	such
plush	shrub	rush	catch	much

Exercise 5.1
Complete the words below by choosing one of the sounds:

ch   sh

rich
flush
plush
chug
hush
crush
shut
shell
champ
catch
clash
crash

1. cra__ __   5. __ __ell   9. __ __ug

2. cla__ __   6. __ __ut   10. plu__ __

3. cat__ __   7. cru__ __   11. flu__ __

4. __ __amp   8. hu__ __   12. ri__ __

Exercise 5.2
Circle a sound to make a real word (there is one per line):

1. pa__   sh   ch   tch
2. cra__   sh   ch   tch
3. bla__   st   sh   p
4. sta__   st   sh   ch
5. ha__   ch   st   tch
6. gl__   in   ad   ash
7. sh__   ip   an   id
8. ch__   ip   it   ag
9. fa__   sh   ch   st
10. st__   ick   ot   eck

stick
fast
chip
ship
glad
hatch
stash
blast
crash
patch

Exercise 5.3
Write the words for the pictures below:

1.   __ __ __ __

2.   __ __ __ __ __

3.  __ __ __ __ __

4.  __ __ __ __

lamp, stump, plant, milk

Exercise 5.4
Read the following sentences to your student and have him/her choose the words that makes sense:

latch	scratch	chin	stamp
switch	hatch	catch	splash

1. To mail a letter, you will need a _____ .

2. The fisherman will try to _____ a fish.

3. The egg will _____ soon.

4. The messy baby had food on his _____ .

5. When you jump into a pool, you make a _____ .

6. You _____ an itch.

7. We secured the door with a _____ .

8. Use the _____ to turn the light on and off.

Exercise 5.5
Read the instructions, on the left, to your student:

1. Change a letter in the word so that it becomes what a baseball player does when throwing a ball to the batter:

patch _____

2. Change a letter in the word so it becomes something that people use to start a fire:

hatch _____

3. Change a letter in the word so it becomes the word for when two cars hit each other with a large force:

trash _____

pitch, match, crash

Exercise 5.6
Fill in the blanks to spell the words for the pictures below:

1. _ _ _ _ _

2. _ _ _ _

3. _ _ _ _

4. _ _ _ _ _

5. _ _ _

6. _ _ _ _

7. _ _ _ _ _

8. _ _ _ _ _ _

9. _ _ _ _

10. _ _ _ _ _

11. _ _ _

12. _ _ _ _ _

13. _ _ _ _ _

14. _ _ _

15. _ _ _ _

16. _ _ _

brush, chin, lash, witch, can, fish, patch, crutch, ship, pitch, pan, match, chips, box, chop, map

Exercise 5.7
Do the dictations for this lesson at www.yourkidcanread.com.

The /th/ Sound

As mentioned in the last lesson, sometimes certain groups, or pairs, of letters make up certain sounds that we have to remember. In the last lesson we looked at 'ch' and 'sh', in this lesson, we will look at 'th'.

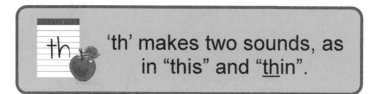

'th' makes two sounds, as in "this" and "thin".

<u>th</u>at   <u>th</u>an   <u>th</u>in   pa<u>th</u>   ma<u>th</u>

Read the following nonsense words:

thag	thog	thush	pith	rith
thig	thim	poth	puth	roth

Mixed practice:

chin	batch	sham	rash	bath
chat	scratch	shim	rich	path
chop	hatch	shot	itch	thatch
catch	hash	crash	thin	stitch

Review:

best - bets	mets - stem	scab - cabs
crash - cash	nest - nets	sham - mash
drop - prod	nit - tin	ship - hips
fats - fast	nod - don	slap - pals
felt - left	pats - past	slit - silt
fist - fits	pest - pets	step - pets
lest - lets	posh - shop	tap - pat
lost - lots	pots - stop	test - sets

Exercise 6.1
Read the following sentences to your student and have him or her choose the word that makes sense and write it on the line:

math	catch	than	thin	stitch
bath	box	this	wish	broth

1. The opposite of fat is _____.

2. _____ is the girl's favorite subject.

3. To get clean, you can take a _____.

4. _____ is the way to camp.

5. Try to _____ the ball.

6. Make a _____ on a shooting star.

7. The woman had to _____ the hole in the pocket.

8. We put the kittens in a _____.

9. When I am sick, I drink hot chicken _____.

10. He is taller _____ I am.

---

a ➡ o

In many words, an 'a' will sound like a short 'o'. Below are some examples. We will see more as we progress through this book.

wash	salt	halt	want
watch	swap	calm	false

-31-

Exercise 6.2
Read the sentences to your student, omitting the word choices.
Have your student circle the word that makes sense:

1. The bird's **nest / nets** is up in the tree.

2. The dress had purple polka **bots / dots**.

3. The chef used **stop / pots** and pans.

4. What happened yesterday is in our **pats / past**.

5. The lumberjack used his axe to **spilt / split** the wood.

6. The little puppy was **lost / lots**.

7. If you catch on fire, you should stop, **drop / prod**, and roll.

8. The opposite of slow is **fats / fast**.

9. The past tense of "feel" is **left / felt**.

10. The coach told him to do the **bets / best** that he could.

Exercise 6.3
Circle a sound to make a real word (there is one per line):

1. pa__   ch   th

2. pa__   tch   th

3. ba__   ch   th

4. sa__   st   sh

5. ra__   ch   sh

6. ma__   th   ch

7. fi__   tch   sh

8. swi__   th   tch

9. swi__   sh   ch

10. di__   sh   ch

dish
swish
switch
fish
math
rash
sash
bath
patch
path

Exercise 6.4

Read the sentences to your student, omitting the word choices.
Have him/her read and circle the word that makes sense:

1. **Shut / Ship** the door when you leave.

2. The car **crush / crash** was on the news.

3. If you go hiking, stay on the **nest / path**.

4. If you get the chicken pox, you shouldn't **scratch / wish**.

5. **Cash / Chop** the lettuce for the salad.

6. When you blow out the candles, make a **rash / wish**.

7. Add **salt / fish** and pepper to the soup.

8. Before you eat you should **wash / crash** your hands.

9. In an emergency, you must stay **clam / calm**.

10. **This / Then** is the first time I saw the Statue of Liberty.

Exercise 6.5

Fill in the blanks to spell the words for the pictures below:

1. _ _ _ _ _ _

2. _ _ _ _

3. w_ _ _

4.  p_ _ _

5. _ _ _ _

6. $\dfrac{64}{8} = 8$ m_ _ _ _

switch, bath, wash,
path, flag, math

Exercise 6.6

Do the dictations for this lesson at www.yourkidcanread.com.

-33-

The /nk/ Sounds

Normally, 'n' makes the /n/ sound as in "nest". However, here, the 'nk' makes a different sound. It makes the sound /nk/ as in "sink".

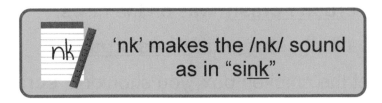

'nk' makes the /nk/ sound as in "si<u>nk</u>".

Read the following to the student and then have him/her read the sounds back to you.
The 'a' in 'ank' is long, all other vowels are short.

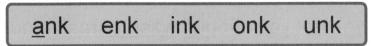

<u>a</u>nk   enk   ink   onk   unk

Remember, put the new sounds on flash cards and have the student read them every day until they are mastered.

s<u>ank</u>   p<u>ink</u>   h<u>onk</u>   h<u>unk</u>

Read the following:

blank	flank	mink	rank	stank
brink	hunk	dunk	rink	stink
clunk	junk	pink	shrink	stunk
drink	link	punk	sink	tank

Review:

bath	catch	hatch	prank	slim
blink	chunk	honk	raft	spank
brim	drank	match	shrank	thank
back	drunk	patch	shrink	think
bank	fast	plank	shrunk	wink

Review (watch for reveral issues):

bad	dib	pop	dab	bod
dad	dip	pip	bob	bop

Read the following:

1. He will chat with me.
2. The flag went up with a swish.
3. I went to the bank with Jim to get cash.
4. The skunk ran on the path.
5. He has to thank you.
6. If you scratch the rash, then it will itch.
7. He drank the pink drink.

Often, a student will think that a /dr/ is from a 'jr'.
There are **no** words that have 'jr'.

 jr - dr ✓ <u>dr</u>ink

Also, students often think that a /tr/ is from a 'chr'.
There are **no** words that have a 'chr',
where 'ch' has the /ch/ sound, as in "chop".

chr - tr ✓ <u>tr</u>unk

Exercise 7.1
Circle the words that are correctly spelled:

1.	jrip	drip	4.	trap	chrap
2.	chrip	trip	5.	drag	jrag
3.	drag	jrag	8.	jrop	drop

drop
drag
trap
drag
trip
drip

Exercise 7.2
Read the following sentences to your student, omitting the unfinished words. Have your student select the correct sounds to complete each words (sounds can be used more than once):

ank	enk	ink	onk	unk

1. A **sk**_____ can make a bad smell!

2. The elephant uses its **tr**_____ to get food.

3. My bother and his friend **dr**_____ all the milk.

4. **P**_____ is my favorite color.

5. I will go to the ice skating **r**_____ on Saturday.

6. The fish really **st**_____ up the house.

7. **H**_____ the horn on the car to alert other cars.

8. The dirty dishes are in the **s**_____.

9. The wool sweater **shr**_____ when I washed it.

10. The dollar store sells a lot of **j**_____.

skunk, trunk, drank, Pink, rink, stunk, Hong, sink, shrank, junk

Exercise 7.3
Fill in the blanks to spell the words for the pictures below:

1.   _ _ _ _

4.   _ _ _ _

2.   _ _ _ _

5.   _ _ _ _ _

3.   _ _ _ _

6.   _ _ _ _

tank, pink, drink, sink, trunk, bank

-36-

Exercise 7.4
Read the following sentences to your student, omitting the unfinished words. Have your student select the correct sounds to complete each words (sounds can be used more than once):

sh   ch   th

1. I had to stop and _____**ink** how to get home.

2. He rode his bike on the dirt **pa**_____ .

3. The girl likes to _____**at** on-line with her friend.

4. We waved at the _____**ip** as it sailed away.

5. We use ice to _____**ill** our drinks.

6. My wool sweater _____**rank** in the wash.

7. I **wi**_____ you could come over tomorrow.

8. Tonight, I will take a bubble **ba**_____.

think, path, chat, ship, chill, shrank, wish, bath

Exercise 7.5
Circle a sound to make a real word (there can be more than one per line):

1. p____   ink   ank   6. sw____   itch   atch

2. b____   ink   ank   7. h____   itch   atch

3. bl____   ink   ank   8. sn____   itch   atch

4. s____   ink   ank   9. p____   itch   atch

5. r____   ink   ank   10. l____   itch   atch

pink, bank, blank, sink & sank, rink & rank, switch & swatch,
hitch & hatch, snitch & snatch, pitch & patch, latch

Exercise 7.6
Do the dictations for this lesson at www.yourkidcanread.com.

Normally, 'n' makes the /n/ sound as in "nest". However, here, the 'ng' makes a different sound. It makes the sound /ng/ as in "sing".

ng | 'ng' makes the /ng/ sound as in "si<u>ng</u>".

Read the following to the student and then have him/her read the sounds back to you.
The 'a' in 'ang' is long, all other vowels are short.

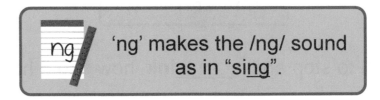

<u>a</u>ng   eng   ing   ong   ung

Remember, put the new sounds on flash cards and have the student read them every day until they are mastered.

s<u>a</u>ng   s<u>ing</u>   s<u>o</u>ng   s<u>u</u>ng

Read the following:

bang	flung	Ping-Pong	spring	string
bling	hung	rang	sling	strong
bring	long	ring	song	stung
cling	lung	sing	sting	wing

Review:

bath	broth	drunk	shrank	stunk
blank	brush	hang	shrink	sunk
blink	bunk	plank	stank	tank
brink	drink	plush	strong	think

Exercise 8.1

Read the following sentences to your student, omitting the unfinished words. Have your student select the correct sounds to complete each words (sounds may be used more than once):

ang	eng	ing	ong	ung

1. The bird will **s**_____ in the early morning.

2. The firecracker went off with a loud **b**_____.

3. The bird will fly by flapping its **w**_____**s**.

4. The rich lady bought a diamond **r**_____.

5. The bee **st**_____ my finger.

6. The three hour movie was too **l**_____.

7. The baseball player will **sw**_____ the bat at the ball.

8. A group of people is called a **g**_____.

9. We use our **l**_____**s** to breathe.

10. We will **h**_____ the picture on the wall.

[answer key, rotated:] sing / bang / wings / sting / long / swung / wings / gang / lungs / hang

Exercise 8.2

Circle a sound to make a real word (there can be more than one per line):

1. r____   ing   ang
2. b____   ing   ang
3. w____   ing   ang
4. h____   ing   ang
5. s____   ing   ang

6. sw____   ing   ink
7. bl____   ang   ank
8. s____   ung   unk
9. th____   ing   ink
10. dr____   ang   ank

[answer key, rotated:] ring & rang / wing / bang / hang / sing & sang / swing / blank / sung & sunk / thing & think / drank

Exercise 8.3
Fill in the blanks to spell the words for the pictures below:

1. _ _ _ _

2. _ _ _ _ _

3. _ _ _ _

4.  _ _ _ _

5.  _ _ _ _

6.  _ _ _ _ _

wing, string, lung, sling, gong, sting

Exercise 8.4
Fill in the blanks to spell the words for the pictures below:

1. _ _ _ _

2. _ _ _ _ _

3. _ _ _ _ _ _

4. _ _ _ _

5. _ _ _ _

6. _ _ _ _

wink, crank, splash, ring, sink, bank

Exercise 8.5
Read the words to your student and have him/her identify if the vowel sound is long or short:

1. beast	long / short	
2. jump	long / short	
3. shot	long / short	
4. peck	long / short	
5. peak	long / short	

6. poke	long / short	
7. lock	long / short	
8. lick	long / short	
9. like	long / short	
10. note	long / short	

long
long
short
short
long

long
short
short
short
long

Exercise 8.6

Read the following sentences to your student, omitting the unfinished words. Have your student select the correct sounds to complete each words (sounds may be used more than once):

> **ank   onk   unk   sh   ch**

1. It is polite to say "please" and "th_____ - you".

2. He cut a **ch**_____ of cheese and gave it to the mouse.

3. The man put the suitcases in the **tr**_____ of his car.

4. The car lost control and had a bad **cra**_____.

5. If you have a lot of money, you are **ri**_____.

6. We had to go to the **b**_____ to get money.

7. The boy liked to **h**_____ the horn on his bicycle.

8. The twins slept in **b**_____ beds.

9. The fish swam in the **t**_____.

10. We played a **pr**_____ on our teacher.

11. The ship hit an iceberg and **s**_____.

12. For soccer, you wear _____**in** guards.

13. To answer the question, you must fill in the **bl**_____.

14. The boxer punched the man in his _____**in**.

thank, chunk, trunk, crash, rich, bank, honk, bunk, tank, prank, sank, sh, blank, chin

Exercise 8.7

Do the dictations for this lesson at www.yourkidcanread.com.

Lesson 9

The /ck/ Sounds

When you hear the /k/ sound **right** after a **short** vowel,
it is *usually* from the two letters 'ck'. These letters can be
in the middle of a word, or at the end of a word.

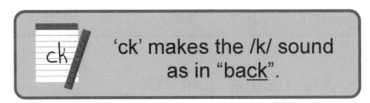

'ck' makes the /k/ sound
as in "ba<u>ck</u>".

*Read the following to the student and then
have him/her read them back to you.*
All vowels are short.

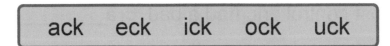

ack   eck   ick   ock   uck

*As with all new sounds and rules, put them on flash cards and
have the student read them every day until they are mastered.*

st<u>ack</u>   sp<u>eck</u>   st<u>ick</u>   st<u>ock</u>   st<u>uck</u>

Read the following:

back	flock	muck	sock	struck
black	heck	neck	speck	tack
brick	lock	pluck	stack	track
check	luck	sick	stick	trick
clock	mock	slick	stuck	tuck

Read the following:

1. Stack the bricks on the shelf.
2. He stuck the stick into the mud.
3. Wish me luck on my math test.
4. The ticket was in my pocket.
5. The truck had a lock in the back.

A Workbook for Dyslexics - Cheryl Orlassino   -42-   Copyrighted material; not to be copied or distributed.

Exercise 9.1
Read the following sentences to your student, omitting the unfinished words. Have your student select the correct sounds to complete each words (sounds may be used more than once):

ack	eck	ick	ock	uck

1. I got **st**_____ in the mud.

2. We have to set the **cl**_____ back an hour.

3. The soldier will be **b**_____ home soon.

4. The ice-cream **tr**_____ went down the road.

5. The boy felt **s**_____ and stayed home from school.

6. Jim has to **p**_____ for the trip.

7. Janet threw the **r**_____ into the ocean.

8. The fog was so **th**_____ that night.

9. The **br**_____ house was strong.

10. The **d**_____ swam in the pond.

11. Your teacher will **ch**_____ your homework.

12. He will neatly **st**_____ the books on the table.

13. At night, the mother will **t**_____ the boy into bed.

14. The hen will **p**_____ at the ground.

15. The store doesn't have my favorite chips in **st**_____.

16. The night sky was pitch **bl**_____.

stuck, clock, truck, sick, pack, rock, thick, brick, duck, check, stack, tuck, peck, stock, black

Read the two syllable words below:

locket	rocket	trucking	tricking
packet	socket	stocking	tucking
ticket	backing	mocking	slacking

 Students often confuse 'ck' and 'nk' sounds within words. Have your student read the words below:

bank - back	rack - rank
clank - clack	stink - stick
crack - crank	pick - pink
stack - stank	brink - brick
hank - hack	puck - punk
rank - rack	link - lick
stuck - stunk	tack - tank
plunk - pluck	slink - slick

Exercise 9.2
Write the words for the pictures below:

1. _ _ _ _

2. sn_ _ _

3. s_ _ _

4. r_ _ _

5. _ _ _ _

6. _ _ _ _ _

7. _ _ _ _ _

8. _ _ _ _ _

9. _ _ _ _

10. k_ _ _

sock, snack, sick, rock, duck,
truck, clock, block, tack, kick

Exercise 9.3
Read the following clues to the student and have him or her write the new word on the line:

1. Change the word so it becomes something that swims on a pond:

    stuck _____

2. Change the word so it becomes the slang word for a dollar:

    truck _____

3. Change the word so it becomes something you wash dishes in:

    stink _____

4. Change the word so it becomes something that is worthless and takes up space:

    dunk _____

    duck, buck, sink, junk

Exercise 9.4
Circle a sound to make a real word (there can be more than one per line):

1. sl___   ack   ick   uck
2. b___   ack   ick   uck
3. st___   ack   ick   uck
4. sn___   ack   ick   uck
5. bl___   ack   ick   uck
6. sh___   ack   ick   uck
7. l___   ack   ick   uck
8. sm___   ack   ick   uck

slack, slick
back, buck
stack, stick, stuck
snack, snuck
black
shack
lack, lick, luck
smack

-45-

Exercise 9.5

Read the following sentences to your student, omitting the unfinished words. Have your student select the correct sounds to complete each words (sounds can be used more than once):

ang	eng	ing	ong	ung

1. The bird **s**_____ a sweet song.

2. I didn't have the **str**_____**th** to keep on running.

3. It won't be **l**_____ until summertime.

4. I got **st**_____ by a bee when I was planting flowers.

5. The little girl likes to play on the **sw**_____.

6. If you lift weights, you will get **str**_____.

7. Yesterday, I **h**_____ the picture on the wall.

8. Please **br**_____ your game to my house.

9. The phone was in my pocket when it **r**_____.

10. If the answer is not right, then it is wr_____.

Exercise 9.6

Circle the words that have the /oo/ sound as in "boo" (hint: there are three):

does	to	he	the
was	has	do	you

Exercise 9.7

Do the dictations for this lesson at www.yourkidcanread.com.

'ay' *always* makes the long 'a' sound.

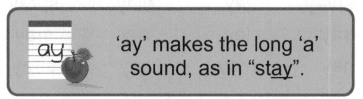

'ay' makes the long 'a' sound, as in "st<u>ay</u>".

d<u>ay</u>	w<u>ay</u>	pl<u>ay</u>
tod<u>ay</u>	sw<u>ay</u>	aw<u>ay</u>*

* The first 'a' in "away" sounds like /uh/.

In a *few* words, 'ey' also makes the long 'a' sound.

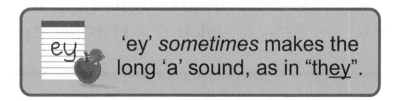

'ey' *sometimes* makes the long 'a' sound, as in "th<u>ey</u>".

gr<u>ey</u>	pr<u>ey</u>	conv<u>ey</u>	surv<u>ey</u>*
th<u>ey</u>	h<u>ey</u>	ob<u>ey</u>*	

* Read these words to your student, since some sounds/rules in these words have not yet been taught.

Read the following:

1. I will pay the man with cash.
2. She will bring the tray to me.
3. The kitten will play with the string.
4. The month of May is in the spring.
5. The man will stay with his truck.
6. The stray cat drinks milk.
7. If I am away, then I am at the bank.

Review:

array	day	hey	pay	slay	sway
astray	display	jay	play	spray	today
bay	fray	lay	ray	stay	tray
clay	hay	may	say	stray	way

bank	tank	stink	junk	sprang	swing	hung
blank	drank	blink	spunk	bring	sung	strong
crank	pink	flunk	sang	fling	lung	strength

bled	chill	cram	glum	plop	shop	stop
box	chip	crash	hitch	plum	shrimp	such
champ	chop	drat	much	rich	snitch	trip
chap	crab	fish	pitch	shin	spot	trot

Exercise 10.1

Circle sounds to make real words (there may be more than one per line):

1.	sn__	ack	ay	uck
2.	bl__	ack	ay	uck
3.	sw__	ack	ay	uck
4.	tr__	ack	ay	uck
5.	pr__	ack	ay	uck
6.	d__	ack	ay	uck
7.	str__	ack	ay	uck
8.	sm__	ack	ay	uck
9.	l__	ack	ay	uck
10.	cl__	ack	ay	uck

snack, snuck
black
sway
track, tray, truck
pray
day, duck
stray, struck
smack
lack, lay, luck
clack, clay, cluck

Exercise 10.2

Read the instructions to your student, and have him/her write the new word on the lines:

1. Change the word so it becomes what you serve food on:

   sway _____

2. Change the word so it becomes something you do to a dragon:

   lay _____

3. Change the word so it's something you do to framed pictures:

   bang _____

4. Change the word so it becomes the organ we use to breathe with:

   stung _____

5. Change the word so it becomes something that a chicken says:

   duck _____

6. Change the word so it becomes the opposite of the color white:

   back _____

7. Change the word so it becomes something that lasts 24 hours:

   way _____

8. Change the word so it becomes the season after winter:

   sing _____

tray, slay, hang, lung, cluck, black, day, spring

Exercise 10.3
Fill in the letters to make the words for the pictures below:

1. _ _ _

2. _ _ _ _

3. _ _ _ _

4. _ _ _

5. _ _ _ _

6. _ _ _ _

7. _ _ _ _

8. _ _ _

9. _ _ _ _ _

10. _ _ _ _

11. _ _ _

12. _ _ _

13. _ _ _ _

14. _ _ _ _

15. _ _ _ _

16. _ _ _ _

17. _ _ _ _ _

18. _ _ _ _ _

19. _ _ _ _

20. _ _ _ _ _

fox, pray, duck, pot, tent, tray, trap, pig, truck, tack, fan, bed, drip, ring, rock, lung, brick, stump, belt, plant

Exercise 10.4
Do the dictations for this lesson at www.yourkidcanread.com.

'oo' has three different sounds,
but it usually has the /oo/ sound
as in "spooky boo"!

Boo!

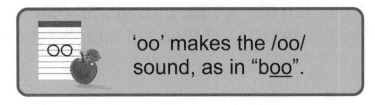

'oo' makes the /oo/
sound, as in "b<u>oo</u>".

c<u>oo</u>l   r<u>oo</u>t   s<u>oo</u>n   t<u>oo</u>   m<u>oo</u>n

Read the following words, where 'oo' has the /oo/ as in "boo" sound:

baboon	broom	fool	room
balloon	caboose	gloom	root
bloom	choose	hoop	snoop
boon	cool	loop	shoot
boot	doom	pool	soon
booth	droop	proof	zoom

Below are the exceptions,
where 'oo' has a different sound:

hood	hook	look
wood	took	book
good	shook	foot

blood   flood

Usually 'oo' sounds like /oo/ as in "boo", so try it that way,
then ask yourself if that's a word you know.
If not, change the word a bit so it becomes a word you do know.

There are a few other ways to get the /oo/ sound besides using 'oo'. Below are words where the 'ou' maks the /oo/ sound. Remember, long 'u' also makes the /oo/ sound.

gr<u>ou</u>p   s<u>ou</u>p   w<u>ou</u>nd   thr<u>ou</u>gh

Note that the 'gh' in "through" is silent.
We will see more of these in later lessons.

Read the following:

1. The chicken soup was good.
2. The ticket booth was next to the pool.
3. The mad man shook his fist at me.
4. The boot does not fit on my foot.
5. The fish is on the hook.
6. I want to look at the book.
7. The group of kids ran through the room.

Exercise 11.1
Complete the words below:

1. _ _ _ _

5.  _ _ _ _

2.  _ _ _ _ _

6.  _ _ _ _

3.  _ _ _ _ _

7.  _ _ _ _ _

4. _ _ _ _

8. _ _ _ _

moon, spoon, broom, spool,
boot, pool, stool, loop

Exercise 11.2

Circle the letters that make a real word, there may be more than one per line:

1. st___ oop ool oon
2. sp___ oop ool oon
3. h___ oop ool oon
4. f___ oop ool oon
5. w___ oop ool oon
6. t___ oop ool oon
7. m___ oop ool oon

stoop, stool
spool, spoon
hoop
fool
wool
tool, toon
moon

Exercise 11.3

Read the sentences to your student, omitting the word choices. Have your student read both words and circle the one that makes sense:

1. The flower will **broom / bloom** in the spring.
2. The past tense of shake is **shook / took**.
3. The past tense of take is **brook / took**.
4. My friend will be back **spoon / soon**.
5. We had enough **moon / room** for everyone.
6. The fish was caught on the **foot / hook**.
7. The past tense of stand is **hood / stood**.
8. When it rains too much, the street may **food / flood**.
9. Your heart will pump **blood / broom** throughout your body.
10. Sweep the floor with a **boom / broom**.

Exercise 11.4

Read the following sentences to your student, omitting the unfinished words. Have your student select the correct sounds to complete each words (sounds can be used more than once):

ay	ack	ank	atch	ang	ash

1. For the side dish, I had to **m**_____ the potatoes.

2. We had to **p**_____ for the trip.

3. The phone **r**_____ three times.

4. On Thursday nights, we take out the **tr**_____.

5. I needed money so I could **p**_____ for my ticket.

6. The baby chick will soon **h**_____.

7. The old house was nothing more than a **sh**_____.

8. We had to put gas in the car's **t**_____.

9. Don't accidentally **b**_____ your knee on the table.

10. When I do my laundry, I have to **m**_____ my socks.

11. I jumped in the pool and made a huge **spl**_____.

12. The man will **st**_____ the bricks in neat rows.

13. The baseball player tried to **c**_____ the ball.

14. The people in the church bowed their heads to **pr**_____.

mash, pack, rang, trash, pay, hatch, shack, tank, bang, match, splash, stack, catch, pray

Exercise 11.5

Do the dictations for this lesson at www.yourkidcanread.com.

The /qu/ Sound & Confused Vowels

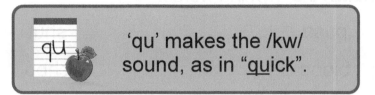

qu 'qu' makes the /kw/ sound, as in "quick".

quit   quack   quick   quest

Read the following:

1. You must be quick to catch the rat.
2. Put the quilt on the bed.
3. The duck in the pond will quack.
4. The man will quit his job today.
5. I am on a quest to get a good book.

Confused Vowels

Very often, words do not follow the rules. Below are cases where the words have an 'a' that sounds like a short 'o'.
There are many more words where this happens, however the simple, one syllable words are listed below:

bald	palm	squash	swap	want
calm	quad	squat	swat	wash
false	salt	squall	wad	wasp
halt	scald	swamp	waltz	watch
malt	squad	swan	wand	watt

Normally, short 'u' sounds like /uh/ as in "umbrella", however, below are words where the 'u' has the same sound as in "took":

put   push   bush   mush

The word "what" is another word with a confused vowel:

what = /wut/

Exercise 12.1
Draw lines to match the rhyming words:

1.	push	shut
2.	blood	chop
3.	rush	crook
4.	took	pray
5.	food	mood
6.	what	fool
7.	hood	hush
8.	they	stood
9.	swap	bush
10.	pool	flood

push-bush, blood-flood, rush-hush, took-crook, food-mood,
what-shut, hood-stood, they-pray, swap-chop, pool-fool

Exercise 12.2
Circle the sounds to make real words. There may be more than one per line:

1. qu___	ock	it	ick
2. pl___	am	ot	uck
3. sp___	ot	it	uck
4. br___	am	ing	uck
5. fl___	ing	ash	um
6. sw___	ick	esh	ing
7. gr___	ick	ip	ick
8. dr___	ip	ink	ank

quit, quick
plot, pluck
spot, spit
bring
fling, flash
swing
grip
drip, drink, drank

Exercise 12.3
Read the following sentences to your student, omitting the unfinished words. Have your student select the correct sounds to complete each words (sounds are used more than once):

ay	oo	ick	ash

1. We took the sailboat out on the **b**_____.

2. In the fall, the weather starts to get **c**_____**l**.

3. In the summer, I will swim in my **p**_____**l**.

4. He likes to **pl**_____ video games.

5. The **s**_____ boy stayed home from school.

6. Every night, I take out the **tr**_____.

7. Do not **cr**_____ your new car.

8. The dog will do a **tr**_____ to get a treat.

9. We went to the **z**_____ to see the animals.

10. I was allergic and broke out in a **r**_____.

11. The dog will play fetch with the **st**_____.

12. We had to go to the store to buy **f**_____**d**.

13. The month after April is **M**_____.

14. Before you eat, **w**_____ your hands.

15. I **t**_____**k** my dog for a walk.

16. We went to **l**_____**k** for the lost kitten.

bay, cool, pool, play, sick, trash, crash, trick, zoo, rash, stick, food, May, wash, took, look

---

-57-

Review:

block	flop	look	shook	stack
boot	fool	milk	sit	stamp
clump	group	plank	soup	stomp
cool	hack	plot	soon	string
drip	hook	rank	spilt	strung
drop	lack	shack	splat	stump
flood	lock	shock	split	took

Exercise 12.4

Read the clues to your student and have him/her write the new word on the line:

1. Change two letters in the word so that it becomes another word for "fast":   trick   _____

2. Change a letter in the word so that it becomes the word for something you do with a framed painting: rang   _____

3. Change the word so it becomes something you eat soup with: soon   _____

4. Change one letter in the word so it becomes something people do when they leave their jobs: quiz   _____

5. Change the word so it becomes something that you use to sweep with: room   _____

quick, hang, spoon, quit, broom

Exercise 12.5

Do the dictations for this lesson at www.yourkidcanread.com.

The /nch/ Sounds

Read the sounds below to your student,
then have him/her read them back.
All vowels are short.

anch	ench	inch	onch	unch

ranch   bench   pinch   conch   lunch

Read the following:

bench	bunch	drench	lunch	quench
blanch	clench	flinch	munch	ranch
branch	conch	hunch	pinch	wench
brunch	crunch	inch	punch	winch

Review:

bald	crip	flask	plant	snug
bask	crisp	glad	plot	swat
blip	crud	grip	plump	tram
brisk	drag	melt	salt	trap
crab	drug	milk	scrap	trim
cramp	flab	palm	spun	trip
crib	flag	plan	snag	wisp

Read the following:

1. We sat on a bench to rest.
2. The lunch was in a basket.
3. Jim will bring the drink.
4. We will watch the ducks swim.
5. Jack sat on a stool in the room.
6. Add a pinch of salt to the soup.

Exercise 13.1

Circle a sound to make a real word; there may be more than one per line:

1. p____   anch   ench   inch   unch

2. b____   anch   ench   inch   unch

3. br____   anch   ench   inch   unch

4. st____   anch   ench   inch   unch

5. cr____   anch   ench   inch   unch

6. qu____   anch   ench   inch   unch

7. dr____   anch   ench   inch   unch

8. r____   anch   ench   inch   unch

9. fl____   anch   ench   inch   unch

10. h____   anch   ench   inch   unch

punch
flinch
ranch
drench
quench
crunch
stench
branch, brunch
bench, bunch
pinch, punch

Exercise 13.2

Complete the /nch/ words below:

1. p_ _ _ _

4. l_ _ _ _

2. w r_ _ _ _ _

5. _ _ _ _ _

3. _ _ _ _ _ _

6. _ _ _ _

pinch, wrench, branch,
lunch, bench, inch

Exercise 13.3

Read the following sentences to your student, omitting the unfinished words. Have your student select the correct sounds to complete each words (sounds are used more than once):

uck	unk	ick	unch	oo

1. The smart girl was **qu**_____ to raise her hand in class.

2. We saw a **bab**_____**n** at the **z**_____.

3. The dog tried to **l**_____ my face.

4. We **sn**_____ into the theater to see the show.

5. He had a **h**_____ that it would rain today.

6. A wrench is **t**_____**l**.

7. Bring a sweater, the night will be **c**_____**l**.

8. Wish me **l**_____ on my test.

9. I slipped on a ice and hurt my **f**_____**t**.

10. If you are very **s**_____ , you should see a doctor.

11. The magician did a magic **tr**_____.

12. Josh gave his girlfriend a **b**_____ of flowers.

13. At noon, it is time to eat **l**_____.

14. The dog chased after the **st**_____.

15. It rained too much and our basement had a **fl**_____**d** .

16. The past tense of "shrink"' is **shr**_____.

quick, baboon & zoo, lick, snuck, hunch, tool, cool, luck, foot, sick, trick, bunch, lunch, stick, flood, shrunk

Exercise 13.4
Read the following sentences to your student, and have your student choose the words that makes sense:

Remember: Many words with 'a' have a short 'o' sound.

want	false	wash	halt	bald
squad	swan	calm	watch	salt

1. You must _____ your hands before you eat.

2. If you have no hair, then you are _____ .

3. When you make soup, you need to add _____.

4. In an emergency, you should stay _____.

5. If it's not true, then it is _____ .

6. The _____ is a graceful bird.

7. She does not _____ to go out for dinner.

8. The babysitter has to _____ the child on Saturday.

9. Another word for "stop" is _____ .

10. The cheerleading _____ won the competition.

Exercise 13.5
Do the dictations for this lesson at www.yourkidcanread.com.

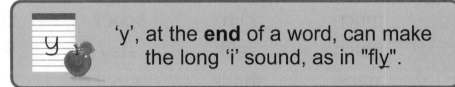

We can get a long 'i' sound with the letter 'y', at the end of a word, or with the letters 'igh'.

'y', at the **end** of a word, can make the long 'i' sound, as in "fl<u>y</u>".

cr<u>y</u>   sp<u>y</u>   fl<u>y</u>   tr<u>y</u>   dr<u>y</u>

'igh' can make the long 'i' sound, as in "h<u>igh</u>".

h<u>igh</u>   s<u>igh</u>   r<u>igh</u>t   br<u>igh</u>t

Note that '<u>eigh</u>' makes the long 'a' sound and will be covered in a later lesson.

Read the following:

buy	dry	guy	sly
by	dye	my	spy
bye	fly	pry	try
cry	fry	shy	why

| bright | high | might | right | sight |
| fight | light | night | sigh | thigh |

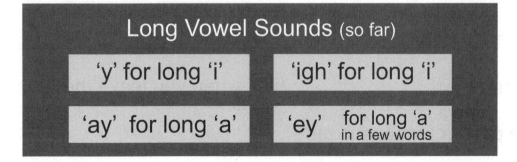

Long Vowel Sounds (so far)

| 'y' for long 'i' | 'igh' for long 'i' |
| 'ay' for long 'a' | 'ey' for long 'a' in a few words |

Review:

blood	long	quack	shrink	such
brook	look	quest	snatch	sung
fetch	match	quick	snuck	sway
flood	much	rich	spook	tack
flung	notch	said	stay	tank
hatch	pack	shack	stool	they
hey	pitch	shook	strength	trunk
hook	plank	shoot	strong	wash

Exercise 14.1

Read the following sentences to your student, and have your student choose the words that makes sense:

light	spy	night	watch
tank	fly	trunk	tight

1. Last _____ we went to bed very late.

2. Next summer, we will _____ in an airplane.

3. I have to _____ my little brother later.

4. The fish swam in the _____ .

5. The double-agent was a secret _____.

6. My sweater shrunk and was now too _____.

7. Turn the _____ off when you leave the room.

8. We put our luggage in the _____ .

Exercise 14.2
Finish the words using 'igh' or 'y' for the long 'i' sound:

1. sp_____

2. sunl_____

3. n_____

4. fl_____

5. cr_____

6. th_____

spy, sunlight, night, fly, cry, thigh

Exercise 14.3
Read the following sentences to your student, and have your student circle the word that makes sense:

1. If you wear glasses, you have poor eye- **fright / sight**.

2. The two boys had a **fright / fight** over who was faster.

3. I **bright / might** go to the movies on Saturday night.

4. The loud noise gave me a **fight / fright**.

5. The opposite of low is **high / fly**.

6. The sun is very **light / bright**.

7. I had a **might / slight** headache.

8. The baby will **cry / fly** if she is tired.

9. A heavy breath is called a **high / sigh**.

10. He had to **ply / pry** the lid off the can.

Exercise 14.4
Do the dictations for this lesson at www.yourkidcanread.com.

The 'oi' and 'oy' Sound

Both 'oy' and 'oi' have the same sound: /oi/ as in "boy" and "boil". Usually, 'oy' comes at the <u>end</u> of the word (such as boy) or at the <u>beginning</u> (such as "oyster"), while 'oi' is *usually* in the <u>middle</u> of the word.

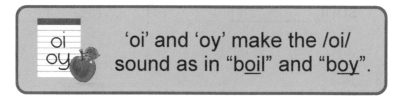

'oi' and 'oy' make the /oi/ sound as in "b<u>oi</u>l" and "b<u>oy</u>".

b<u>oy</u>   pl<u>oy</u>   b<u>oi</u>l   c<u>oi</u>n

Read the following:

boy	ploy	coy	
joy	soy	toy	
boil	foil	joint	soil
broil	groin	joist	spoil
coil	hoist	oil	toil
coin	join	point	void

Words With Two or More Syllables

To read words that have more than one syllable, you should divide and conquer!

basket ➡ bask | et

contrast ➡ con | trast

dentist ➡ dent | ist

Read the two syllable words below:

basket	drastic	packet	sonic
bracket	gasket	plastic	submit
bucket	jacket	pocket	ticket
contest	locket	racket	trumpet
contrast	mishap	rocket	vanish
dentist	napkin	socket	wicked

* The 'a', in the /oi/ words below, sounds like /uh/.

<u>a</u>noint   <u>a</u>void

<u>a</u>ppoint   loy<u>a</u>l

Read the following sounds:

ick	ang	ay	ung
ink	ock	igh	anch
ing	onk	oo	atch
ack	ong	unk	itch
ank	oy	uck	inch

Exercise 15.1
Complete the words (each one has the /oi/ sound):

1. c __ __ __

2. b__ __

3. t__ __

4. p__ __ __ __

5. c__ __ __

6. b__ __ __

coin, boy, toy, point, coil, boil

Exercise 15.2

Circle the sounds to make real words (there may be more than one per line:

1. t___   oy   oil   ank

2. sp__   y   oy   oil

3. spr__   oy   ink   ay

4. br__   ink   oy   oil

5. b__   ank   oy   oil

6. j__   oy   ink   unk

7. pr__   ink   ank   oy

8. s__   oil   ank   ink

9. st__   oy   ay   ink

10. c__   ank   oin   oy

Exercise 15.3

Read the sentences to your student and have him/her circle the word that makes sense:

1. The hot water began to **point / boil**.

2. I had to sit on the **broil / bench** to tie my shoe.

3. We use **foil / oil** to heat the house.

4. The little girl grew one **inch / pinch** last year.

5. A plant needs good **spoil / soil** to grow.

6. We **dank / drank** soda at the party.

7. The couple had a baby **boy / boil**.

Exercise 15.4

Read the instructions to your student and have him/her write the new word on the line:

1. Change the word to be the place where people keep their pet fish:

bank _____

2. Change the word so it becomes another word for "garbage":

crash _____

3. Change the word so it becomes the name for the second meal of the day:

crunch _____

4. Change the word so it becomes something that people swim in:

fool _____

5. Change the word so it becomes something babies do when they are upset:

spy _____

6. Change the word so it becomes something you put food on:

wish _____

7. Change the word so it becomes something that birds and airplanes do:

sly _____

8. Change the word so it becomes another word for "fast" and "speedy":

thick _____

9. Change the word so it becomes something kittens like to play with:

bring _____

tank, trash, lunch, pool, cry, dish, fly, quick, string

Exercise 15.5

Do the dictations for this lesson at www.yourkidcanread.com.

In this lesson we will see when vowels are paired with the letter 'r'. These are very common sounds that can be anywhere in a word.

Read the sounds below to your student.
Note that 'er', 'ir', and 'ur' sound the same.

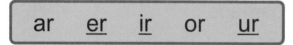

ar   er   ir   or   ur

Remember to put sounds, introduced in the lessons, on flash cards and review before each lesson.

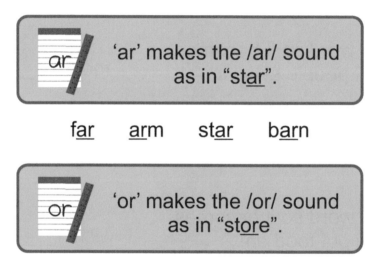

'ar' makes the /ar/ sound as in "star".

far   arm   star   barn

'or' makes the /or/ sound as in "store".

* 'or' is also a word, as in "this *or* that".

for   form   storm   born

Read the following:

bar	dark	market	park	start
barn	far	mart	port	stark
born	farm	normal*	pork	storm
car	form	orbit	scar	tar
cart	formal*	par	shark	tart
corn	mark	part	short	torn

* The 'a', in most words with 'al', has the /uh/ sound.

Exercise 16.1

Complete the words below (words can have 'ar' or 'or'):

1. c __ __ __

2. b __ __ __

3. __ __ m

4. h __ __ __

5. sh __ __ __

6. ch __ __ __

7. j __ __

8. f __ __ __

9. c __ __

10. st __ __

11. ch __ __ __

12. th __ __ __

corn, barn, arm, horn, shark, chart,
jar, farm, car, star, charm, thorn

Exercise 16.2

Circle the sound(s) to make a real word. There may be more than one or none per line:

1. st__	art	ort	9. f__	arm	ork
2. p__	art	ort	10. p__	arm	ork
3. ch__	art	ort	11. ch__	arm	ork
4. sh__	art	ort	12. c__	arm	ork
5. sp__	ark	orm	13. sh__	ark	orn
6. b__	ark	orm	14. t__	ark	orn
7. st__	ark	orm	15. d__	ark	orn
8. f__	ark	orm	16. c__	ark	orn

start
part, port
chart
short

farm, fork
pork
charm
cork

spark
bark
stark, storm
form

shark
tork
dark
corn

The "do nothing" 'e'

Most words that have /or/, as the **final sound** in a word, have a "do nothing 'e'" at the end:

adore	core	more	shore	store
before	explore	ore	snore	swore
bore	fore	pore	sore	tore
chore	ignore	score	spore	wore

Exercise 16.3
All 'or' words below have a "do nothing" 'e'. Complete the words:

1. sc __ __ __

2. c __ __ __

3. sn __ __ __

4. 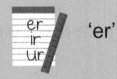 st __ __ __

score, core, snore, store

 'er', 'ir', and 'ur' all make the same sound.

st<u>er</u>n   f<u>ir</u>m   t<u>ur</u>n

When writing words with the /er/ sound, it's difficult to know which pair to use, which is why you need to become familiar with the words.

er {	st<u>er</u>n	enter	quicker	perk	her
	fern	master	stronger	jerk	perch
ir {	b<u>ir</u>d	first	skirt	shirt	firm
	birth	stir	dirt	third	girl
ur {	sp<u>ur</u>	turn	surf	church	disturb
	slur	burn	burp	curl	curb

Exercise 16.4

Complete the words below. Note that the words can have 'er', 'ir, or 'ur'.
Refer to the list, on the previous page, if needed:

1. b __ __ __

6. s __ __ __

2. sh __ __ __

7. sk __ __ __

3. t __ __ __

8. f __ __ __

4. **3**rd th __ __ __

9. **1**st f __ __ __ __

5. ch __ __ __ __

10. st __ __

bird, shirt, turn, third, church,
surf, skirt, fern, first, stir

⭐ Some words do not follow the rules.
If you are reading a word and
it doesn't sound like a word you know,
change it slightly, so it becomes
a word you do know: ⭐

*Read the sentences below to your student, but have
him/her read the underlined word:*

My mother will go to **work** on Monday.

work = /werk/

The two countries were at **war**.

war = /wor/

There was an earth **worm** in the dirt.

worm = /werm/

-73-

Read the following:

black	cooler	fight	marker	stink
blacker	corn	fighter	quick	stinker
bright	corner	light	quicker	strong
brighter	crack	lighter	spoil	stronger
broil	cracker	long	spoiler	tink
broiler	farm	longer	stick	tinker
cool	farmer	mark	sticker	under

Other /or/ Words

The words below have the /or/ sound, however, they have **extra** vowels, which are **not** needed:

door
floor   } These all have a "do nothing" 'o'.
poor

your
four   } These all have a "do nothing" 'u'.
pour

Exercise 16.5

Circle the word which is correctly spelled:

1.	cor	core	6.	ignore	ignor
2.	flore	floor	7.	por	poor
3.	store	stor	8.	dor	door
4.	mor	more	9.	shore	shor
5.	your	yor	10.	bor	bore

were & we're

These two words are often confused.

were: This is the /w/ sound and the /er/ sound with a "do nothing" 'e' at the end.

w<u>er</u>e

we're: This a contraction for "we are". In a contraction, two words are pushed together, a letter gets popped out, and an apostrophe takes its place.

out → in
we are = we're

* Add these words to your flash cards for daily review *

Exercise 16.6
Read the following and circle the word that makes sense:

1. The stars **was / were** in the night sky.

2. It **was / were** a cool day.

3. **Were / We're** going to the park.

4. Four kittens **we're / were** in the box.

5. The girl **was / were** in her bedroom.

6. The group of kids **was / were** in the pool.

7. Why **were / we're** they in a fight?

8. After dinner, **were / we're** going to the play a game.

*Your student should read **all** sentences, unless otherwise specified.*

were, was, We're, were, was, were, were, we're

Exercise 16.7
Do the dictations for this lesson at www.yourkidcanread.com.

Pinch yourself, here come the ouches!
There are two ways to get the /ou/ sound as in "ouch".

Both 'ou' and 'ow' make the /ou/ sound.

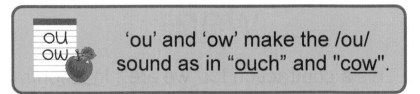

> ou
> ow
>
> 'ou' and 'ow' make the /ou/ sound as in "<u>ou</u>ch" and "c<u>ow</u>".

o<u>u</u>t   p<u>ou</u>t   l<u>ou</u>d

pl<u>ow</u>   c<u>ow</u>   n<u>ow</u>

Read the following 'ou' words:

about	count	foul	mouth	south
blouse	counter	grouch	our	spout
bound	crouch	house	out	tout
cloud	douse	joust	pouch	trout
clout	encounter	loud	pout	
couch	flounder	mouse	shout	

around	bound	ground	mound	round
astound	found	hound	pound	sound

Read the following 'ow', as /ou/ words:

allow	cow	frown	owl	shower
bow	cower	gown	plow	towel
brown	crowd	growl	powder	town
chowder	down	how	power	vow
clown	flower	now	prowl	wow

'ow' also makes the long 'o' sound.

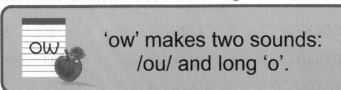

'ow' makes two sounds:
/ou/ and long 'o'.

<u>grow</u>   sh<u>ow</u>   bl<u>ow</u>   b<u>ow</u>l

* Words that end with the long 'o' sound, *usually* end with 'ow'.*

Read the following 'ow', as long 'o' words:

arrow	flown	low	sow
below	follow	mow	slow
blow	glow	narrow	stow
blown	grow	own	swallow
borrow	grown	pillow	throw
bowl	growth	row	tomorrow
crow	hallow	show	tow
flow	hollow	snow	yellow

Spelling Hints - 'ou' or 'ow' for /ou/

1. If the /ou/ sound is at the <u>end of a word</u>, then it is probably '<u>**ow**</u>'.

h<u>ow</u>   c<u>ow</u>   n<u>ow</u>

2. If the /ou/ sound is in the <u>middle of a word</u>, try writing it both ways and see which way looks right. The more you read, the better you'll get.

cl<u>ou</u>n ✗
cl<u>ow</u>n ✓

3. If the word has the /out/ sound, always use 'ou'.

sh<u>out</u>   cl<u>out</u>   ab<u>out</u>   sc<u>out</u>   p<u>out</u>

Lesson 17 - The 'ou' and 'ow' Sounds

In some words, the 'ou' does **not** make the /ou/ sound.

s**ou**p	c**ou**ld	d**ou**ble
gr**ou**p	w**ou**ld	tr**ou**ble
thr**ou**gh	sh**ou**ld	

---

should** **w**ould** **c**ould**

In the words above, the 'ould' makes the same sound as the 'ood' in "good".

Spelling hint: for 'ould' use the following:

"**o**wls **u**se **l**aundry **d**etergent"

should	**w**ould	**c**ould
owls use	owls use	owls use
laundry	laundry	laundry
detergent?	detergent?	detergent?

Exercise 17.1
Circle the correct answer:

1. 'ay' makes:	long 'a'	short 'a'
2. 'er' sounds like:	/or/	/ir/
3. 'ar' sounds like:	/or/	'r'
4. 'igh' sounds like:	long 'i'	short 'i'
5. 'ow' can sound like:	long 'o'	short 'o'
6. 'ir' sounds like:	/or/	/er/
7. 'oi' sounds like:	long 'o'	'oy'
8. 'ow' can sound like:	/ou/	/oi/

long 'a',
/ir/,
'r',
long 'i'
long 'o',
/er/,
'oy',
/ou/

Exercise 17.2
Complete the words below (all have 'ou' for the /ou/ sound):

1. sh__ __ __

2. m__ __ __ __

3. cl__ __ __

4. m__ __ __e

5. h__ __ __e

6. c__ __ __ __

shout, mouth, cloud, mouse, house, couch

Exercise 17.3
Complete the words below (all have 'ow' for the /ou/ sound):

1. c__ __

2. __ __l

3. cr__ __ __

4. sh__ __ __ __

5. fl__ __ __ __

6. p__ __ __ __

cow, owl, crown, shower, flower, power

Exercise 17.4
Complete the words that have the long 'o' sound from an 'ow':

1. b__ __ __

2. cr__ __

3. b__ __

4. bl__ __

bowl, crow, bow, blow

Exercise 17.5
Circle the correct way to spell the following words:

1.	now / nou	6.	pownd / pound
2.	lowd / loud	7.	sownd / sound
3.	about / abowt	8.	growmd / ground
4.	clowd / cloud	9.	bownd / bound
5.	crowd / croud	10.	brown / broun

crowd
cloud
about
loud
now

brown
pound
ground
sound
pound

Exercise 17.6
Read the clues to your student and have him/her write the new word on the lines:

1. Change the word so it becomes a word for when two people are angry, they have a ?

sight _____

2. Change the word so it becomes the opposite of day:

light _____

3. Change the word so it becomes another word for 16 ounces:

sound _____

4. Change the word so it becomes a place where people live:

brown _____

5. Change the word so it becomes the opposite of fast:

low _____

6. Change the word so it becomes what you walk on in your house:

door _____

fight, night, pound, town, slow, floor

Exercise 17.7
Do the dictations for this lesson at www.yourkidcanread.com.

'ew' *usually* has the /oo/ sound, as in "new".

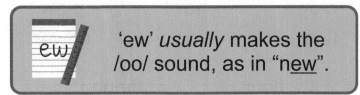

'ew' *usually* makes the /oo/ sound, as in "n<u>ew</u>".

gr<u>ew</u>   dr<u>ew</u>   ch<u>ew</u>   n<u>ew</u>

In a *few* words, 'ew' sounds like 'u'.

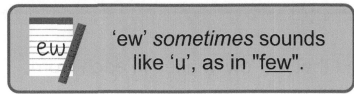

'ew' *sometimes* sounds like 'u', as in "f<u>ew</u>".

f<u>ew</u>   sp<u>ew</u>   sk<u>ew</u>   curf<u>ew</u>   neph<u>ew</u>*

* The 'ph' sound has not yet been taught, however many students know this sound already. See if your student can read it.

> The words where 'ew' sounds like 'u' are very few,
> and most are listed above.

Read the following:

blew	crew	flew	new	skew
brew	drew	grew	screw	stew
chew	few	mildew	shrew	strew

Read the following:

1. The bird flew away from me.
2. The wind blew the dirt onto the floor.
3. The cow will chew her food.
4. Last night we had stew for dinner.
5. My brother has a new toy for his pet bird.

Review of /ou/, as in "ouch", words:

allow	clown	growl	owl	shower
brow	crown	howl	plow	towel
brown	flower	now	power	town

around	flour	hound	round
bound	found	mound	sound
count	ground	pound	sour

Exercise 18.1
Circle the sound that the 'ow' makes in each word:

1. sn<u>ow</u>   long 'o'   /ou/
2. <u>ow</u>l   long 'o'   /ou/
3. sh<u>ow</u>   long 'o'   /ou/
4. fl<u>ow</u>er   long 'o'   /ou/
5. bl<u>ow</u>   long 'o'   /ou/
6. h<u>ow</u>l   long 'o'   /ou/

7. n<u>ow</u>   long 'o'   /ou/
8. br<u>ow</u>n   long 'o'   /ou/
9. sl<u>ow</u>   long 'o'   /ou/
10. gr<u>ow</u>   long 'o'   /ou/
11. gr<u>ow</u>l   long 'o'   /ou/
12. dr<u>ow</u>n   long 'o'   /ou/

Exercise 18.2
Circle a sound to make a real word (there may be more than one per line):

1. t___   ow   ew
2. st__   ow   ew
3. n__   ow   ew
4. thr___   ow   ew
5. b__   ow   ew

6. pl___   ow   ew
7. gl__   ow   ew
8. fl__   ow   ew
9. gr__   ow   ew
10. sn__   ow   ew

Exercise 18.3
Read the instructions to your student:

1. Change the word so it becomes the opposite of "old":

grew _____

2. Change the word so it becomes something you sweep with:

room _____

3. Change the word so it becomes something that floats in the sky:

loud _____

4. Change the word so it becomes the opposite of weak:

long _____

5. Change the word so it becomes the opposite of smile:

crown _____

6. Change the word so it becomes the opposite of "low":

sigh _____

7. Change the word so it becomes the opposite of "near":

car _____

new, broom, cloud, strong, frown, high, far

Exercise 18.4
Draw lines to match the rhyming words:

1. wood   foul

2. new   pay

3. cry   zoo

4. they   could

5. owl   go

6. skirt   hurt

7. blow   high

wood-could
new-zoo
cry-high
they-pay
owl-foul
skirt-hurt
blow-go

Review:

batter	flounder	quack	slower	thicker
belong	formal	quench	spoiler	this
birthday	gloom	quick	sound	turn
blacker	hard	quilt	struck	trinket
carport	hound	quit	summer	twirler
door	hatchet	scoop	should	winter
faster	hammock	shorter	thinker	within
found	port	slick	thank	without

Exercise 18.5
Read the sentences and circle the word that makes sense:

1. The **birth / bird** slept in a nest.

2. We have a **flew / few** things to do this morning.

3. We were going too **quick / quack**.

4. In the morning the boy took a **chowder / shower**.

5. The quilt was on my bed, in my **broom / room**.

6. Last **summer / scooter** we went on a short trip.

7, We put the rug on the **floor / ground**.

8. The thick fog will blanket the **yard / crown**.

9. How much milk **stood / should** we get?

10. My **house / horse** is down the block, around the corner.

Exercise 18.6
Do the dictations for this lesson at www.yourkidcanread.com.

So far we've seen letter pairs that
make long vowel sounds, such as:

ay, igh, ow (as in "snow")

In this lesson, we will see how having a vowel
near another vowel, can turn the first vowel
long. There are two ways to do this:

1. **V**owel - **C**onsonant - **V**owel
2. **V**owel - **V**owel

Part 1: Vowel - Consonant - Vowel (VCV)

When a vowel is one jump to the left of another
vowel, then the vowel on the left becomes LONG.
In the words below, the 'o' becomes long.

hope   hoping

Notice that it can be *any* vowel, not just 'e',
that can turn the vowel on the left long.

Read the following (remember, long 'u' usually sounds like /oo/):

pin - pine	can - cane	spin - spine	rat - rate
rip - ripe	mop - mope	fin - fine	hop - hope
cap - cape	shin - shine	mad - made	hid - hide

bike	rule	kite	brake	spike
fake	take	poke	make	time
dine	shake	rake	like	crime

Exercise 19.1
Read the sentences and circle the word that makes sense:

1. The sick boy said that he felt **fin / fine**.

2. We went for a **rid / ride** on the horse.

3. If your pants are too tight, they may **rip / ripe**.

4. We went to the park to fly our **kite / kit**.

5. His pet **snack / snake** was in the box.

6. We had to **tack / take** our brother out for lunch.

7. The man will **stake / stack** the bricks.

8. The girl will try to **back / bake** a cake.

9. The man will **rob / robe** the bank.

10. The young girl **slide / slid** down the pipe.

Exercise 19.2
Circle a sound to make a real word (there may be more than one sound per line:

1. t___	ick	ir	ime	
2. st__	oy	ir	ine	
3. sh__	out	er	ine	
4. br__	oy	ow	ime	
5. b__	oi	ow	ite	
6. pl__	oy	ow	ate	
7. gl__	ick	ow	ime	
8. sp__	out	ow	ine	

spout, spine
glow
ploy, plow, plate
bow, bite
brow
shout, shine
stir
tick, time

Part 2: Vowel Teams (V V)

When two vowels are **next to each other**, the first one *usually* becomes **long** and the second one is *usually* silent. In the word below, 'o' becomes long and the 'a' is silent.

foam

The Common Vowel Teams

a	e	i	o	u
ai	ee	ie	oa	ue
ea				

 When vowel teams go walking, the **first** one does the talking!

Read the following (remember, long 'u' usually sounds like /oo/):

<u>ai</u>d	b<u>ee</u>f	b<u>ea</u>ch	b<u>oa</u>t	d<u>ie</u>
air	creep	bean	board	lie
brain	feed	cheat	coach	tie
chain	deep	clear	goal	lied
fail	meet	dear	goat	contin<u>ue</u>
mail	need	dream	loan	argue
stair	keep	fear	poach	blue
sprain	sleep	leash	roach	clue
hail	teeth	real	roast	fuel
paid	week	speak	soap	glue

A Workbook for Dyslexics - Cheryl Orlassino — -87- —

Below are the **most common** vowel teams, however, **any** two vowels can team up together.

a	e	i	o	u
ai	ee	ie	oa	ue

ea

The first vowel becomes **long** and the second vowel is *usually* silent. *Sometimes* the second vowel has a **short** vowel sound.

fr<u>u</u>it	'ui' is not a common vowel team. The 'u' is long (/oo/), the 'i' is silent.
l<u>i</u>on	'io' is not a common vowel team. The 'i' is long, and the 'o' is NOT silent, it has the **short** 'o' sound.
qu<u>i</u>et	The 'u' is part of the 'qu' sound and is NOT part of a vowel team. Here, 'ie' is a team. The 'i' is long and the 'e' has the **short** 'e' sound.

Exercise 19.3
Circle the answers (there may be more than one per line):

1. Which letter pairs have the long 'a' sound?   oa   ay   ai

2. Which letter pairs have the long 'e' sound?   ee   oy   ea

3. Which letter pair has the long 'o' sound?   oy   io   oa

4. Which letter pairs have the /oi/ sound?   oy   oi   io

5. Which letter pair has the long 'i' sound?   ei   ie   igh

ay & ai, ee & ea, oa, oy & oi, ie & igh

ee ?or ea

In order to know which vowel team to use,
you must become familiar with the words.

ee		ea	
agree	kneel	appear	gear
bee	peek*	beach	heal*
beef	queen	bead	heat
beep	reek	beam	leader
between	see	bean	leaf
bleed	seed	beard	leak
breeze	seek	beast	lean
cheek	seem*	beat	leap
cheese	seen	bleach	leash
creek*	sheep	bleak	mean
creep	sheet	breathe	meat*
deep	sleep	cheap	near
deer*	sneeze	cheat	neat
fee	speed	clean	peach
feed	steel*	clear	peak*
feel	street	creak*	peanut
feet	sweet	cream	please
flee*	teen	crease	preach
free	teeth	deal	reach
freeze	three	dear*	rear
greed	tree	dream	scream
greet	tweet	each	seat
heel*	weed	eagle	seem*
jeep	week*	ear	steal*
keep	weep	east	steam
knee	wheel	easy	stream
		fear	teach
		flea*	treat
		freak	weak*

*These words are homophones.
Not all homophones are noted.

Mark this page for reference
for future lessons.

Exercise 19.4

For each word below, identify the long vowel sound, and write it on the line:

1.	quaint ____		13.	fear ____
2.	spray ____		14.	sleep ____
3.	load ____		15.	flow ____
4.	show ____		16.	teeth ____
5.	plain ____		17.	grow ____
6.	sight ____		18.	sway ____
7.	boat ____		19.	diet ____
8.	soak ____		20.	spy ____
9.	sheet ____		21.	pie ____
10.	frame ____		22.	timer ____
11.	toad ____		23.	mower ____
12.	snow ____		24.	fright ____

Exercise 19.5

Circle the word that makes the most sense:

1. The loud noise came from the **house / flower**.

2. I had to go home to get my **bucket / bike**.

3. We go together like a hammer and **nail / screw**.

4. There were no clouds in the **blank / blue** sky.

5. If you want to play the game, you must follow the **rule / leader**.

Exercise 19.6

Do the dictations for this lesson at www.yourkidcanread.com.

Adding the Suffix - 'ing'

There are two rules you must know to add an 'ing' to a word:

Rules for Adding 'ing'

1. Adding 'ing' to a short vowel word:

   Make sure the vowel 'i' in 'ing' will not
   make a short vowel long.
   If that happens, you must:

   Double the consonant to protect the short vowel.

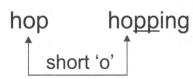

hop   hopping

short 'o'

*Two body
guards to
protect the
short vowel.*

   *This does NOT always apply to words
   with *more* than *one* syllable.

 The following consonants are **never** doubled:

c h j k q v w x y

---

2. Adding 'ing' to a word ending with 'e':

   Drop the 'e' and add the 'ing'.

   tape   taping

   one letter jump - 'a' is long

   For all other words, just add the 'ing'.

   spy   spying
   play   playing

Short vowel words that need protecting: Need 2 body guards!

ship - shi<u>pp</u>ing	win - wi<u>nn</u>ing
rid - ri<u>dd</u>ing	hit - hi<u>tt</u>ing
run - ru<u>nn</u>ing	rip - ri<u>pp</u>ing
clap - cla<u>pp</u>ing	put - pu<u>tt</u>ing

Words that end with 'e': Get rid of the 'e'!

take - taking	wake - waking
hide - hiding	bite - biting
fake - faking	make - making
note - noting	mope - moping

All other words: Just add 'ing'

pack - packing	risk - risking
try - trying	boat - boating
plant - planting	eat - eating
rent - renting	sleep - sleeping

Protecting Short Vowels in Multisyllable Words

For words with more than one syllable, if the last syllable is not stressed (accented) then you do **not** double the last consonant to protect a short vowel.

Last syllable is NOT stressed, <u>do not double the consant</u>	Last syllable IS stressed, <u>double the consant</u>
happe<u>n</u> - happe<u>n</u>ing	begi<u>n</u> - begi<u>nn</u>ing
ope<u>n</u> - ope<u>n</u>ing	submi<u>t</u> - submi<u>tt</u>ing
butto<u>n</u> - butto<u>n</u>ing	transmi<u>t</u> - transmi<u>tt</u>ing

A Workbook for Dyslexics - Cheryl Orlassino　　　-92-

Exercise 20.1

Add 'ing' to the following words:

1. rake _____

2. slap _____

3. cry _____

4. sit _____

5. sleep _____

6. run _____

7. kick _____

8. swim _____

9. swing _____

10. slide _____

raking, slapping, crying, sitting, sleeping,
running, kicking, swimming, swinging, sliding

Exercise 20.2

Fill in the vowel pairs for the common long vowel teams:

a   e   i   o   u

□   □   □   □   □

□

ai, ee & ea, ie, oa, ue

Read the following:

star - stare   bar - bare   car - care   par - pare   far - fare

rare	declare	snare	firmware
mare	welfare	share	flatware
dare	blare	flare	hardware
square	spare	glare	aware

air   chair   pair

fair   hair   staircase

Exercise 20.3

Choose the word that makes sense, and then change it by adding 'ing':

1. The rabbit is _____ up the hill.
    [bite , hop]

2. The rabbit is _____ to get a carrot.
    [hope , spit]

3. The girl was _____ a black horse.
    [ride , swim]

4. The man is _____ his child play in the park.
    [let , run]

5. The boy is _____ the dog.
    [pet , stir]

6. The cook is _____ a cake.
    [back , bake]

7. As of today, we were _____ the contest.
    [win , ride]

8. Jim was _____ his bike.
    [fix , smell]

9. I am _____ to go home later.
    [go , tape]

10. If it gets hot out, can we go _____ ?
    [ride , swim]

11. The bird was _____ over my house.
    [fly , wash]

12. The girl is _____ on the bed.
    [sing , sit]

13. He was _____ the car around on the highway.
    [bite , turn]

14. The woman is _____ her drink.
    [slip , sip]

hopping, riding, letting, petting, baking, winning, turning, fixing, going, swimming, flying, sitting, turning, sipping

Exercise 20.4
Complete the following "silent 'e'" words below:

1. _ _ _ _

2. _ _ _ _

3. _ _ _ k _

4. _ _ k _

5. _ _ _ _

6. c _ _ _

pipe, tape, snake, rake, rope, cone

Exercise 20.5
Write the following vowel team words below:

1. _ _ _ _

2. _ _ _ _

3. **3** _ _ _ _ _

4. _ _ _ _

5. _ _ _ _

6. _ _ _ _

7. _ _ _ _ _

8. _ _ _

9. _ _ _ _

10. _ _ _ _ _

11. _ _ _

12. _ _ _ _ _

pail, glue, three, sail, tree, nail,
teeth, pie, rain, snail, pie, train

Exercise 20.6
Do the dictations for this lesson at www.yourkidcanread.com.

To make a word past tense, we usually add the letters 'ed' to the end of the word. We also have irregular past tense words that do not get an 'ed' added, but the words themsevles change. First we will look at words where 'ed' is added.

Read the past tense words below:

hand - handed   list - listed

rest - rested   wait - waited

Notice - in words that end with a /t/ or /d/ sound, when they become past tense, by adding 'ed', you hear the /ed/ sound, and another syllable gets added to the word.

Now read the past tense words below:

jump - jumped   hop - hopped

shop - shopped   wish - wished

In these words, you do **not** hear the 'ed', and, instead, the word sounds like a **one syllable** word ending with /t/ or /d/.

jumped = /jumpt/

shopped = /shopt/

Irregular Past Tense Verbs

Below are *some* examples of past tense words that are irregular:

wake - woke	take - took
run - ran	shake - shook
sing - sang	stink - stunk
sleep - slept	eat - ate

Exercise 21.1
Read the words, and circle the words where you hear the 'ed' as /ed/ (there are 4):

baked	coped	hiked	traded	stacked
banged	cracked	licked	needed	timed
cleaned	hated	liked	rocked	waited

hated, traded, needed, waited

Exercise 21.2
Write the past tense form for the words below. Note these will have **irregular** past tense forms. Use the sentence below to help:

Today I _____, but yesterday I _____.

1. take _____
2. shake _____
3. ride _____
4. spend _____
5. sing _____
6. sting _____
7. hang _____
8. meet _____
9. flee _____

10. shoot _____
11. eat _____
12. go _____
13. drink _____
14. slide _____
15. light _____
16. have _____
17. say _____
18. shrank _____

took
shook
rode
spent
sung
stung
hung
med
fled

shot
ate
went
drank
said
lit
had
said
shrunk

When adding 'ed' to a word, you follow the same rules as you did when adding 'ing', however the third rule is new, and applies to most suffixes (except 'ing').

Rules for Adding 'ed'

1. Adding 'ed' to a short vowel word:

    Make sure the vowel 'e' in 'ed' will not make a short vowel long. If that happens, you must:

Double the consonant to protect the short vowel.

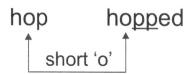

hop   hop<u>p</u>ed

short 'o'

Two body guards to protect the short vowel.

*This does NOT always apply to words with *more* than *one* syllable.

 The following consonants are **never** doubled:

c h j k q v w x y

2. Adding 'ed' to a word ending with 'e':

    Drop the original 'e' and then add the 'ed'.

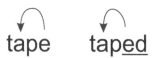

tape   tap<u>ed</u>

one letter jump - 'a' is long

3. If the word ends with a **consonant followed by a 'y'**:

    Turn the 'y' into an 'i', and then add the 'ed'.

cr<u>y</u>   cr<u>ied</u>

Read the following:

rest - rested	jump - jumped	plan - pla<u>nn</u>ed
last - lasted	stamp - stamped	pat - pa<u>tt</u>ed
hand - handed	clamp - clamped	cram - cra<u>mm</u>ed
sport - sported	bump - bumped	sin - si<u>nn</u>ed
plant - planted	rock - rocked	pin - pi<u>nn</u>ed
rant - ranted	pick - picked	brag - bra<u>gg</u>ed
jet - jetted	tuck - tucked	flag - fla<u>gg</u>ed
part - parted	long - longed	cry - cr<u>i</u>ed
farm - farmed	belong - belonged	spy - sp<u>i</u>ed
harm - harmed	ding - dinged	try - tr<u>i</u>ed
charm - charmed	wing - winged	reply - repl<u>i</u>ed

> If the word is **not** an irregular verb, you **must** add the 'ed',
> to make it past tense - **even if you do not hear the 'ed'.**

For words with more than one syllable, only
double the last consonant to protect the short vowel
if the last syllable is **stressed** (or accented):

The last syllable is not stressed:		The last syllable is stressed:
happen - happened	pardon -pardoned	prefer - prefe<u>rr</u>ed
listen - listened	edit - edited	occur - occu<u>rr</u>ed
glisten - glistened	beckon - beckoned	permit - permi<u>tt</u>ed
travel -traveled	ticket - ticketed	benefit - benefi<u>tt</u>ed
garden - gardened	pocket - pocketed	unplug - unplu<u>gg</u>ed
target - targeted	darken - darkened	incur - incu<u>rr</u>ed

Exercise 21.3

Write the past tense form for the words below. Use the sentence below to help:

Today I _____, but yesterday I _____.

1. cry _____
2. try _____
3. play _____
4. sway _____
5. sip _____
6. lick _____
7. spy _____
8. pin _____
9. plan _____

10. weed _____
11. stamp _____
12. garden _____
13. rake _____
14. bake _____
15. like _____
16. need _____
17. strum _____
18. hum _____

cried tried played swayed sipped licked spied pinned planned

weeded stamped gardened raked baked liked needed strummed hummed

Exercise 21.4

Write the vowel teams on the lines to complete the words below:

1. We went out to sea on a **b __ __ t.** [oa , ou]

2. The scared girl **scr __ __ med.** [ee , ea]

3. The peacock fanned out his colorful **t__ __l.** [ay , ai]

4. She wanted to **k __ __ p** the locket in the safe. [ee , ea]

5. I did not **sl __ __ p** last night due to the noise. [ee , ea]

oa, ea, ai, ee, ee

Exercise 21.5

Circle the word that is correctly spelled (you may have to refer to the list on the other page):

1. happen   happe<u>n</u>ed / happe<u>nn</u>ed

2. listen   liste<u>n</u>ed / liste<u>nn</u>ed

3. open   ope<u>n</u>ed / ope<u>nn</u>ed

4. travel   trave<u>l</u>ed / trave<u>ll</u>ed

5. prefer   prefe<u>r</u>ed / prefe<u>rr</u>ed

6. target   targe<u>t</u>ed / targe<u>tt</u>ed

7. pardon   pardo<u>n</u>ed / pardo<u>nn</u>ed

8. edit   edi<u>t</u>ing / edi<u>tt</u>ing

9. permit   permi<u>t</u>ing / permi<u>tt</u>ing

10. benefit   benefi<u>t</u>ed / benefi<u>tt</u>ed

benefitted
permitted
edited
pardoned
targeted
preferred
traveled
opened
listened
happened

> * Note that in some words, with more than one syllable, the VCV rule does not always apply.
>
> <u>e</u>dit   b<u>e</u>nefit   tr<u>a</u>vel

Exercise 21.6

Fill in the vowel pairs for the common long vowel teams:

a	e	i	o	u
☐	☐	☐	☐	☐
	☐			

ai, ee & ea, ie, oa, ue

Exercise 21.7

Do the dictations for this lesson at www.yourkidcanread.com.

The /nd/ Sounds

In the sounds below, all vowels are short,
except the 'i' in 'ind', which is *usually* long.

and	end	ind	ond	und

h**and**   b**end**   f**ind**   p**ond**   **und**er

*Remember to add new sounds and rules to flash cards, and
review the cards before each lesson.*

Read the following 'ind' words:

bind	find	hind	mind
blind	grind	kind	wind*

---

* This word, "wind", can be read with a short or long 'i'.
Read the sentences below:

<u>Wind</u> the clock to keep it running.

The <u>wind</u> blew the leaves off the trees.

Read the following 'nd' words:

band	find	gland	ponder	send
behind	fond	hand	pretend	thunder
bend	friend	pending	sand	under
fend	fund	pond	second	wonder

Review the 'y' as long 'i' words:

ally	cry	fly	July	ply	sky
apply	defy	fry	magnify	rectify	sly
by	deny	horrify	mortify	rely	spy
classify	dry	identify	multiply	reply	sty
comply	falsify	imply	my	shy	supply

Just like 'ind' has the long 'i' sound for no reason, the three words below also have the long 'i' sound (for no reason):

child   wild   mild

Put these words on flash cards for review until mastered.

Read the following:
1. The thunder was so loud that it shook the house.
2. We were putting our feet in the sand, when the wave came.
3. How did he get the funds for the new car?
4. We need to find where the pond is.
5. They were going to send a brand new box to me.
6. The teacher is fond of the smart girl.
7. A mild wind blew from the north.
8. The woman held the wild child in her arms.

Exercise 22.1
Write the past tense form for the words below:

Today I ___, but yesterday I ___.

1. send _____	9. ride _____
2. find _____	10. spy _____
3. shake _____	11. carry _____
4. marry _____	12. stand _____
5. hurry _____	13. land _____
6. worry _____	14. plan _____
7. pat _____	15. spin _____
8. swim _____	16. march _____

sent
found
shook
married
hurried
worried
patted
swam

rode
spied
carried
stood
landed
planned
spun
marched

Exercise 22.2
Fill in the blanks with one of the following sounds to complete the unfinished words (sounds can be used more than once or not at all):

| and   end   ind   ond   und |

1. I had to **st**_____ in line for a long time.

2. The ducks like to swim on the **p**_____.

3. Mike likes to **sp**_____ his spare cash on food.

4. The lady was very **k**_____ to me.

5. The man was **f**_____ of the sweets.

6. If you look for trouble, you will often **f**_____ it.

7. The **s**_____ from the beach got on my toes.

8. I have to **s**_____ this letter out today.

9. The thunder made the dog hide _____**er** the bed.

10. The man wants to purchase a **br**_____ new car.

11. The little girl likes to **pret**_____ to be a queen.

12. The **sec**_____ the rat saw the cat it ran away.

13. I do not **m**_____ if you sing out loud.

14. The singer wanted to join the **b**_____.

15. The boat sunk and the crew was **str**_____**ed**.

16. The dog was hiding **beh**_____ the truck.

Review of /ou/, 'ow' as long 'o', and /oi/:

account	round	slow	coil	spoil
amount	around	flow	toil	exploit
about	plow	follow	joint	hoist
cloud	town	hollow	point	moist
found	crown	swallow	appoint	asteroid
sound	now	shallow	void	poison
bound	flown	annoy	avoid	noise
mound	grow	royal	cloister	tabloid
hound	grown	oyster	conjoin	toilet

Exercise 22.3

Choose the correct word, and write it on the line:

were	we're

1. _____ going to leave at four o'clock.

2. What _____ you going to do on Sunday?

3. Last September we _____ looking for a new house.

4. I think _____ going to see the show after dinner.

5. Janet said that _____ going to swim in the lake later.

6. The wild animals _____ fighting with each other.

7. _____ taking the sick child to the hospital.

8. _____ you looking at the new website?

We're, were, we're, we're, were, we're, We're, Were

Exercise 22.4

Do the dictations for this lesson at www.yourkidcanread.com.

The /ct/ Sounds

Read the sounds to your student, and then have him/her read them back to you. All vowels are short.

act	ect	ict	oct	uct

f<u>act</u>   inf<u>ect</u>   str<u>ict</u>   d<u>oct</u>or   instr<u>uct</u>

Read the following 'ct' words:

abstract	contract	exact	pact
compact	distract	fact	retract
contact	enact	impact	subtract

aspect	eject	interject	reflect	spectacular
defect	infect	neglect	reject	subject
deject	insect	object	sect	suspect
detect	inspect	project	sector	
direct	intellect	prospect	select	

addict	contradict	derelict	inflict	restrict
afflict	convict	district	picture	strict
conflict	depict	evict	predict	verdict

concoct	octane	octagon	octopus
doctor	nocturnal	October	proctor

abduct	deduct	induct	obstruct
construct	destruct	instruct	product

Remember, review your flash cards every day until the sounds are mastered.

Exercise 23.1

Circle one sound to make a real word. Be careful; sometimes a past tense word sounds like a 'ct' word:

1. b ___	act	end	ict
2. f ___	itch	act	out
3. f ___	ash	ind	ict
4. sn ___	act	acked	icked
5. m ___	ond	and	ind
6. w ___	ect	end	ild
7. ch ___	end	ild	ind
8. str ___	ict	ind	out
9. s ___	ind	igh	out
10. p ___	ond	ict	ild

pond
sigh
strict
child
wild
mind
snacked
find
fact
bend

Exercise 23.2

Complete the words below:

1. ___ ___ ___ or

2. ___ ___ ___ ___ or

3. con___ ___ ___ ___or

4.  dir___ ___ ___ or

5. in___ ___ ___ ___

6. $\begin{array}{r} 56 \\ -4 \\ \hline 52 \end{array}$ sub___ ___ ___ ___ ___

actor, doctor, conductor, director, insect, subtract

Exercise 23.3
Choose a word from the list to complete the sentence:

inspect	evicted	strict	detective	correct
instruct	construct	doctor	protect	project

1. He will _____ the car before he buys it.

2. The teacher had to _____ the papers.

3. The _____ will solve the case.

4. The teacher in that class is too _____.

5. After school you must work on your _____.

6. The boy used a wood box to _____ a race car.

7. Air-bags will help _____ you in a crash.

8. When I got sick, I had to visit the _____.

9. She will _____ you on how to fill out the form.

10. Tenants, who do not pay rent, may get _____.

Exercise 23.4
Circle the past tense form of each word. Be careful; sometimes a past tense word sounds like a 'ct' word:

1.	stack	stact / stacked	5.	trick	trict / tricked
2.	back	bact / backed	6.	tan	tand / tanned
3.	jam	jammed / jamd	7.	grin	grin / grinned
4.	pick	pict / picked	8.	stack	stact / stacked

tricked, tanned, grinned, stacked
stacked, backed, jammed, picked,

Exercise 23.5
Choose the correct letter pairs for each word, and write them on the lines (refer to the ee/ea lists in lesson 19 if needed):

1. n__ __d (ee, ea)   7. l__ __n (ee, ea)

2. k__ __p (ee,ea)   8. qu__ __n (ee, ea)

3. f__ __l (ee, ea)   9. l__ __sh (ee, ea)

4. h__ __t (ee,ea)   10. gr__ __n (ee, ea)

5. m__ __l (ee, ea)   11. t__ __n (ee, ea)

6. sl__ __p (ee, ea)   12. l__ __f (ee, ea)

Exercise 23.6
Draw lines to match the sounds on the left to those on the right that have the same sound:

1.	oi	ea
2.	ur	ay
3.	ai	er
4.	igh	oa
5.	ee	oy
6.	ew	ou
7.	ow1	ie
8.	ow2	oo

Exercise 23.7
Do the dictations for this lesson at www.yourkidcanread.com.

'aw' and 'au' both make the /aw/ sound.

 'aw' and 'au' make the /aw/ sound as in "p<u>aw</u>" and "p<u>au</u>se".

p<u>aw</u>   cl<u>aw</u>   p<u>au</u>se   cl<u>au</u>se

'aw' is *usually* at the **end** of a word.
'au' is *usually* in the **middle** of a word,
and is never at the end of a word.

Read the following:

claw	flaw	law	pawn	saw
dawn	jaw	paw	raw	straw

applaud	cause	haul	launch	pause
author	fraud	haunt	maul	taunt

bec<u>au</u>se   p<u>au</u>se   appl<u>au</u>se   c<u>au</u>se

Note that in the four words above, 's' sounds like /z/.
We will see more on that in another lesson.

Read the following:

1. You may get smarter as you get older.
2. If you hurt your leg, you will have trouble walking.
3. The girl will avoid the boy who taunts her.
4. The car crash was not my fault.
5. We will applaud good acting.
6. The dog gave me his paw.
7. To stay out of jail, you must follow the law.
8. I like to jog at night, because the air is cool.

A Side Note

In the words below, the 'e' does not turn the 'o's long, and the 'o's sound like short 'u':

some = /sum/	none = /nun/
come = /cum/	done = /dun/

Put these words on flash cards for review.

Review (note that in some words, 's' sounds like /z/):

astute	cruise	duet	glue	stupid
barbeque	cure	flute	intrude	suit
bruise	cute	fruit	pure	unite
confuse	due	funeral	rescue	use
continue	duel	fuse	student	value

soup	through	touch	floor	your
group	couple	door	poor	young

Exercise 24.1

Fill in the blanks to spell the words for the pictures below:

1. cr __ __ __

5. dr __ __

2. __ __ __

6. __ __ __ __ __

3. __ __ __

7. __ __ __ __

4. h __ __ __ __

8. __ __ __ __ __

crawl, saw, paw, haunt, draw, straw, claw, yawn

Exercise 24.2
Choose the correct word to complete the sentence:

launch	cause	dawn	jaw
applaud	haul	fraud	author

1. The opposite of dusk is _____.

2. The fake statue was a _____.

3. The truck will _____ the rocks to the site.

4. The boxer punched the man in the _____.

5. The _____ met her fans at the book store.

6. The rocket _____ was at noon.

7. What was the _____ of the fire?

8. The crowd will _____ the actor.

Exercise 24.3
Circle the word that is correctly spelled:

1. wer / were
2. befor / before
3. dor / door
4. floor / flor
5. was / wuz
6. wut / what
7. is / iz

8. stor / store
9. your / yor
10. work / werk
11. more / mor
12. shirt / shert
13. tern / turn
14. therd / third

'all' sometimes has the /awl/ sound.

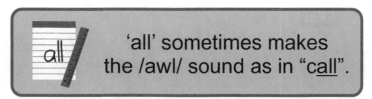

'all' sometimes makes the /awl/ sound as in "c<u>all</u>".

c<u>all</u>   w<u>all</u>   f<u>all</u>

Read the following:

all	wall	call	mall	small
fall	ball	tall	stall	appall

★ In most words, 'al'= /ul/. ★

<u>a</u>live	anim<u>al</u>	mor<u>al</u>	pet<u>al</u>
<u>a</u>loud	equ<u>al</u>	optim<u>al</u>	reg<u>al</u>
<u>a</u>lways	loy<u>al</u>	ov<u>al</u>	riv<u>al</u>

Exercise 24.4

Draw lines to match up the sounds:

1.	igh	ai
2.	aw	oi
3.	oy	ow
4.	ew	oo
5.	ay	er
6.	ur	'r'
7.	ee	ou
8.	ar	ie
9.	oa	au
10.	ow	ea

'alk' has the /awk/ sound only in a *few* words.

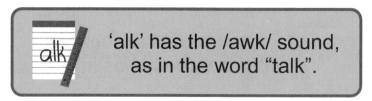

'alk' has the /awk/ sound,
as in the word "talk".

<u>talk</u>   w<u>alk</u>   ch<u>alk</u>   st<u>alk</u>   b<u>alk</u>

The five words above are the only words
that have the /awk/ sound for 'alk'.

Exercise 24.5

Fill in the banks with a word that has one of the sounds in the box below:

> aw   all   alk

1. The horse was kept in the _____.

2. In the _____ we have to rake the leaves.

3. Jane took her dog out for a _____.

4. The man is in jail because he broke the _____.

5. My friend and I _____ for a long time.

6. Children like to _____ with markers.

7. The boy drew on his driveway with _____.

8. The opposite of short is _____.

9. If you are tired, you may _____.

stall, fall, walk, law, talked, draw, chalk, tall, yawn

Exercise 24.6
Circle a sound to make a real word; there may be more than one per line - be careful, some combinations sound like real words but are not:

1. str____   ict   all   alk   awl
2. ch____   act   all   alk   awl
3. t____   uct   all   alk   awl
4. st____   act   all   alk   awl
5. cr____   uct   all   alk   awl
6. w____   act   all   alk   awl
7. f____   act   all   alk   awl
8. sm____   act   all   alk   awl

(upside-down answer key in margin: strict / tall, talk / chalk / stall, stalk / crawl / wall, walk / fact, fall / small)

Exercise 24.7
Circle the word that completes the sentence:

1. There was still **some / come / none / done** work to do.
2. **Some / Come / None / Done** over my house on Thursday.
3. They said we would have **some / come / done** rain today,
4. By five o'clock, we were **some / come / done** with work.
5. When the timer beeped, the cake was **some / come / done**.
6. **Come / None / Done** of the sick children went to school.
7. He was finally **some / come / done** with his project.

Exercise 24.8
Do the dictations for this lesson at www.yourkidcanread.com.

Very often, words ending with
's', 'es', or 'se' end with the /z/ sound.

plays   bushes   noise

Notice how all 's's in the above words end with the /z/ sound.

Read the following; note how 's' sounds like /z/:

advise	chose	fuse	supervise
arise	close	noise	surprise
applause	compose	nose	these
Chinese	comprise	pose	those
choose	confuse	rise	wise

pose   hose   nose   rose

★ Spelling Hint ★

Most words that end with the /z/ or /s/ sounds
(not from double 's' words, such as "miss"),
often have a "do nothing" 'e' at the end:

Read the following words which end with the /s/ sound, and note
the do nothing 'e':

horse	mouse	goose	sense
house	tense	geese	loose

Review:

inspect	quiet	couch	practical	mind
insult	command	pouch	factual	behind
adult	commend	found	own	because
stair	more	sound	grown	blind
fair	come	ground	gown	talk
flair	some	reason	slow	walk
quit	none	season	plow	chalk
quite	done	pleasing	find	crawl

Read the words below, which have 'z's for the /z/ sound:

gaze	size	prize	freeze
graze	fuze	maze	froze

Exercise 25.1
Fill in the missing letters to complete the words:

1. h__ __ __ __

2. h__ __ __ __

3. m__ __ __ __

4. r__ __ __

5. n__ __ __ __

6. n__ __ __

7. h__ __ __

8. g__ __ __ __

horse, house, mouse, rose,
nurse, nose, hose, goose

Exercise 25.2
Circle the sound that the 'se' makes for each word:

1.	pur<u>se</u>	/s/	/z/		8.	advi<u>se</u>	/s/	/z/
2.	nur<u>se</u>	/s/	/z/		9.	rin<u>se</u>	/s/	/z/
3.	tho<u>se</u>	/s/	/z/		10.	cha<u>se</u>	/s/	/z/
4.	crea<u>se</u>	/s/	/z/		11.	ca<u>se</u>	/s/	/z/
5.	tea<u>se</u>	/s/	/z/		12.	ea<u>se</u>	/s/	/z/
6.	the<u>se</u>	/s/	/z/		13.	grea<u>se</u>	/s/	/z/
7.	plea<u>se</u>	/s/	/z/		14.	ba<u>se</u>	/s/	/z/

1. /s/
2. /s/
3. /z/
4. /s/
5. /z/
6. /z/
7. /z/

8. /z/
9. /s/
10. /s/
11. /s/
12. /z/
13. /s/
14. /s/

Exercise 25.3
Read the following and circle the word that makes sense:

1. In the afternoon, I sometimes eat a **snake / snack**.

2. My grandmother and I used to **back / bake** together.

3. The past tense of **take / tack** is "took".

4. Our cat **likes / licks** her fur to keep clean.

5. In the fall, we have to **rack / rake** the leaves.

6. In the summer, we go down to the **lack / lake** to swim.

7. Put the food in the **sack / sake**.

8. You must be quiet, or the infant will **wake / wack** up.

9. Try not to **shack / shake** the bottle of pop.

Exercise 25.4

Change the words below to their past tense form:

Today I ____, but yesterday I ____.

1. sneeze   _____
2. release   _____
3. choose   _____
4. pose   _____
5. advise   _____
6. close   _____
7. skip   _____
8. draw   _____
9. help   _____
10. stop   _____
11. use   _____
12. grow   _____

closed
advised
posed
chose
released
sneezed

grew
used
stopped
helped
drew
skipped

Exercise 25.5

Circle a sound to make a real word (there may be more than one per line):

1. p____   art   ach   elp
2. fl__   ish   ash   ow
3. b__   art   ose   ase
4. dr__   ash   ow   aw
5. sm__   ash   art   ow
6. gl__   ow   ew   ase
7. sh__   ish   ow   art
8. ch__   art   ash   ase
9. d__   ish   ow   art

part
flash-flow
base
draw
smash-smart
glow
show
chart-chase
dish-dart

Exercise 25.6

Do the dictations for this lesson at www.yourkidcanread.com.

In a word, the sound that 'y' makes all depends on where it is:
1. In the **beginning** of a word, 'y' has the /y/ sound as in "yellow".
2. In the **middle** of a word, 'y' sounds like a long or short 'i'.
3. At the **end** of a word, 'y' sounds like a long 'e' or long 'i'.

> beginning: /y/ as in "yellow"
> middle: short or long 'i'
> end: long 'e' or long 'i'

yellow   myth   hype   happy   cry

Read the following; 'y' is at the **beginning**:

yank	yawn	yeast	yellow	yoke
yard	years	yell	yesterday	young

> When reading a word **with 'y' in the middle**:
> substitute an 'i' for the 'y':
> type ➡ tipe

Read the following; 'y' is in the **middle** (substitute an 'i' for the 'y'):

short 'i':

abysmal	hypnotic	syllable	synapse	syrup
abyss	hysteric	symbol	sync	system
acrylic	lynch	symbolic	synonym	tryst
analytic	lyric	symmetric	syntax	
hymn	myth	sympathize	synthetic	

long 'i':

asylum	hybrid	hyper	style	zygote
hydrate	hydrant	pylon	type	
dehydrate	hype	python	typist	

Read the following; 'y' is at the **end**:

<u>long 'i':</u>

ally	classify	guy	ply	sly
amplify	comply	horrify	pry	supply
awry	cry	July	rectify	try
buy	deny	liquefy	rely	unify
by	dignify	modify	satisfy	verify
clarify	fly	my	shy	why

<u>long 'e':</u>

ability	family	money	scary	pretty
alley	fantasy	monkey	fantasy	quirky
bakery	fifty	party	forty	smoky
candy	floppy	partly	sporty	sorry
cozy	funny	hardy	shifty	ugly
daily	happy	story	sunny	worry

 'y' acts like a vowel and can make a nearby vowel long.

tin   t<u>i</u>n<u>y</u>

short 'i'   long 'i'

Therefore, in some words we must double
consonants, to protect short vowels.

su<u>n</u> - su<u>nny</u>

Read the following:

runny	nanny	nutty	snappy	peppy
sunny	penny	ratty	happy	drippy
funny	witty	snotty	hippy	caddy
bunny	chatty	puppy	poppy	ruddy

Remember, in some words, 'ey' makes the long 'a' sound
(we already saw this in an earlier lesson):

conv<u>ey</u>	h<u>ey</u>	pr<u>ey</u>	th<u>ey</u>
gr<u>ey</u>	ob<u>ey</u>	surv<u>ey</u>	wh<u>ey</u>

However, usually 'ey' sounds like long 'e', as in:

all<u>ey</u>	chimn<u>ey</u>	mon<u>ey</u>	turk<u>ey</u>
balon<u>ey</u>	donk<u>ey</u>	monk<u>ey</u>	vall<u>ey</u>

Exercise 26.1
Fill in the missing letters to complete the words:

1. __ __ k __

2. l __ __ __

3. m__ __ __ __ __

4. m__ __ __ __

5. t__ __ __ __ __

6. ch__ __ __ e __

7. __ __ __

8. k __ __

9. p__ __ __

10. b __ __ __

11. d__ __ k__ __

12. __ __ __ __ ow

yoke, lady, monkey, money, turkey, chimney,
fly, key, pony, baby, donkey, yellow

Exercise 26.2
Change the words below as instructed (first go back and review):

	add 'ing'	make past tense
1. fly	_____	_____
2. worry	_____	_____
3. hose	_____	_____
4. deny	_____	_____
5. carry	_____	_____
6. try	_____	_____
7. verify	_____	_____

flew worried hosed denied carried tried verified

flying worrying hosing denying carrying trying verifying

Exercise 26.3
Read the questions out loud and circle the correct answer:

1. The 'y' in "symbol" sounds like: long 'i'   short 'i'

2. The 'y' in "myth" sounds like: long 'i'   short 'i'

3. The 'y' in "try" sounds like: long 'i'   long 'e'

4. The 'y' in "deny" sounds like: long 'i'   long 'e'

5. The 'y' in "happy" sounds like: long 'i'   long 'e'

6. The 'y' in "synthetic" sounds like: long 'i'   short 'i'

7. The 'y' in "syllable" sounds like: long 'i'   short 'i'

8. The 'y' in "hype" sounds like: long 'i'   short 'i'

1) short i, 2) short i, 3) long i, 4) long i, 5) long e, 6) short i, 7) short i, 8) long i

Exercise 26.4
Do the dictations for this lesson at www.yourkidcanread.com.

Lesson 27
Adding the Suffix - 'ly' and 'er'

In earlier lessons, we added the suffix 'ing' and the suffix 'ed' (for past tense words). In this lesson, we will add the suffix 'ly' and the suffix 'er'. When we add a suffix, we are adding an ending to a **root** word, which changes that word.

Part 1: Adding 'ly'

A **verb** is usually a word that expresses an action (such as sing).
An **adverb** is a word that *describes* a verb,
such as "loudly", "softly", or "deeply".

The children sang.
The children <u>softly</u> sang.

Here, the adverb is "softly", which describes the verb "sang".
How did the children sing? They sang softly.

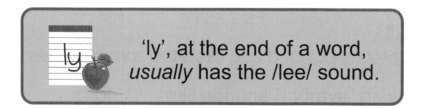

'ly', at the end of a word, *usually* has the /lee/ sound.

happy - happi<u>ly</u>   sad - sad<u>ly</u>   quick - quick<u>ly</u>

Rules for Adding 'ly'

1. If the word ends with a consonant followed by a y, change the 'y' to an 'i', then add the 'ly':

hap**py** - happi**ly**

2. If the word ends with 'le', remove the 'le', then add the 'ly':

simp**le** - simp**ly**

3. Otherwise, just add 'ly':

quick - quick**ly**   sad - sad**ly**   wishful - wishful**ly**

> Note that for words like "happily", you
> **hear** the short 'i' in the word.

Read the following:

angry - angrily	firm - firmly
awful - awfully	hopeful - hopefully
awkward - awkwardly	last - lastly
bashful - bashfully	lazy - lazily
bubble - bubbly	loud - loudly
careful - carefully	real - really
cheerful - cheerfully	safe - safely
close - closely	slow - slowly
complete - completely	tender - tenderly
faithful - faithfully	thankful - thankfully
fearful - fearfully	time - timely
final - finally	wonderful - wonderfully

Exercise 27.1

Add 'ly' to the words below, and write the new words on the lines:

1. _____
   safe

2. _____
   slow

3. _____
   quick

4. _____
   careful

5. _____
   formal

6. _____
   normal

7. _____
   angry

8. _____
   lazy

9. _____
   noisy

10. _____
    mighty

(answers, inverted:)
safely
slowly
quickly
carefully
formally

mightily
noisily
lazily
angrily
normally

<u>Part 2: Adding 'er'</u>

A **noun** is usually a word that is a thing, such as "dog" or "house".
An **adjective** is a word that *describes* a noun,
such as "red", "big", or "loud".

The <u>small</u> dog ran home.

Here, the adjective is "small", which describes the noun "dog".
Adjectives answer the questions:
Whose? How much? Which one? What kind?
The above sentence answers the question: "What kind?"
What kind of dog? A small one.

We add the suffix 'er' to the root word to **compare** two nouns.

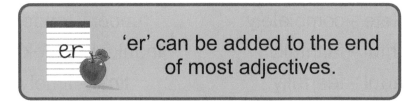

'er' can be added to the end
of most adjectives.

happy - happi<u>er</u>   sad - sadd<u>er</u>   quick - quick<u>er</u>

<u>Rules for Adding 'er'</u>

1. If the word ends with a consonant followed by a y,
change the 'y' to an 'i', then add the 'er'.
Note that the 'i' will sound like a long 'e' in these words.

hap**py** - happi**er**

2. If the word ends with an 'e', add an 'r':

fin**e** - fin**er**

3. Since 'er' starts with a vowel, you may have to double
a consonant to protect a short vowel:

fat - fa**tter**

4. Otherwise, just add the 'er': sick - sick**er**

Note that for words like "happier", the 'i' sounds like a long 'e'.

Read the following:

big - bigger	play - player
funny - funnier	quick - quicker
happy - happier	risky - riskier
lazy - lazier	safe - safer
light - lighter	slow - slower
long - longer	strong - stronger
loud - louder	sunny - sunnier
mighty - mightier	tiny - tinier

Exercise 27.2
Read the sentences below and write the word in bold, adding 'er':

1. You are **loud,** but I am _____ .

2. You are **lucky,** but I am _____ .

3. You are **funny,** but I am _____ .

4. You are **big,** but I am _____ .

5. You are **tan,** but I am _____ .

6. You are **quiet,** but I am _____ .

7. You are **happy,** but I am _____ .

8. You are **noisy,** but I am _____ .

9. You are **strong,** but I am _____ .

louder
luckier
funnier
bigger
tanner
quieter
happier
noisier
stronger

Review:

lest - lets	lost - lots	far - fare	mare - marry
just - juts	quite - quiet	par - pare	store - story
fits - fist	drop - droop	bar - bare	gore - gory
bets - best	shot - shoot	car - care	fur - furry - fury
nest - nets	hop - hoop	scare - scary	star - stare
fast - fats	cop - coop	care - carry	star - starry
clam - calm	scar - scare	sore - sorry	lion - loin

Exercise 27.3

Read the sentences and write the correct form of the word on the line:

1. The girl _____ to pick up the rock.
   try

2. We _____ arrived home.
   safe

3. We _____ to go to the beach later.
   plan

4. The baby was _____ than his brother.
   fat

5. We went _____ in the lake.
   swim

6. We _____ have dessert after dinner.
   normal

7. They _____ the sick boy to the hospital.
   carry

tried, safely, planned, fatter, swimming, normally, carried

Exercise 27.4

Do the dictations for this lesson at www.yourkidcanread.com.

When 'g' has the /j/ Sound

Up to this point, 'g' has had a hard sound, as in "get".
Now we'll see when 'g' has the soft sound, as in "gel".

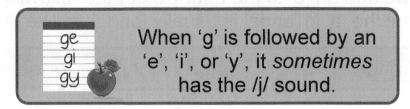

When 'g' is followed by an 'e', 'i', or 'y', it *sometimes* has the /j/ sound.

cage   gist   energy

Read the following:

age	digest	general	giant	large
angel	energy	genetic	gigantic	page
apology	gelatin	gentle	ginger	rage
cage	gems	Germany	gym	stage

There aren't any words in our language that end with a 'j'.
For words that end with /j/, you must have a 'ge'.
And, since the 'e' in 'ge' can make a vowel long,
we add a 'd' to protect the short vowel.

dge

adge	edge	idge	odge	udge

badge   pledge   ridge   lodge   judge

Read the following:

badge	dodge	grudge	lodge	smidge
badger	edge	hedge	partridge	smudge
bridge	fridge	judge	ridge	trudge
budge	fudge	knowledge	sludge	wedge

In an earlier lesson we saw the following sounds:

ang, eng, ing, ong, ung

If we add an 'e' to the end, we get the following:
(Note that the 'a' in 'ange' is usually long, just like in 'ang').

| ange | enge | inge | onge | unge |

range   revenge   fringe   lunge

Read the following:

arrange	fringe	passenger	sponge
challenge	hinge	plunge	stranger
cringe	lunge	rearrange	twinge
danger	messenger	scavenger	vengeful

Exercise 28.1
Fill in the blanks to spell the words for the pictures below:

1.   j _ _ _ _

2.   c _ _ _

3.   b _ _ _ _

4.   b _ _ _ _ r

5.   br _ _ _ _

6.   pl _ _ _ _ r

7.   ang _ _

8.   ang _ _

judge, cage, badge, badger,
bridge, plunger, angel, angle

Multisyllable Words ending with 'age'

In multisyllable words that end with 'age', the 'age' sometimes sounds like /edge/:

advantage	cabbage	damage
average	cartilage	disparage
baggage	cleavage	dosage
bandage	cottage	drainage
beverage	courage	message
blockage	coverage	package

Exercise 28.2

Circle the word that makes sense:

1. The cook added **cottage / cabbage** to the stew.

2. The doctor gave the correct **damage / dosage**.

3. A drink is a **coverage / beverage**.

4. We had to **challenge / change** our costumes for the play.

5. She likes to **arrange / range** the food in the refrigerator.

6. I had a **cabbage / message** in my in-box from my friend.

7. For your final grade, find the **average / avenge** of your tests.

8 The nurse put a **baggage / bandage** on the deep gash.

9. The brave man had a lot of **courage / coverage**.

10. I was a **messenger / passenger** on the road trip.

Exercise 28.3
Circle the sound that makes a real word:

1. j_____   udge   adge
2. br_____   edge   idge
3. l_____   edge   adge
4. sl_____   adge   udge
5. pl_____   edge   idge

6. ch_____   inge   ange
7. arr_____   inge   ange
8. cr_____   inge   unge
9. fr_____   inge   ange
10. pl_____   inge   unge

pledge
sludge
ledge
bridge
judge

plunge
fringe
cringe
arrange
change

Exercise 28.4
Write the past tense form for the words below:

Remember: 'ew' makes the /oo/ sound.

1. The past tense of <u>grow</u> is _____ .

2. The past tense of <u>draw</u> is _____ .

3. The past tense of <u>drink</u> is _____ .

4. The past tense of <u>hang</u> is _____ .

5. The past tense of <u>go</u> is _____ .

6. The past tense of <u>see</u> is _____ .

7. The past tense of <u>find</u> is _____ .

8. The past tense of <u>send</u> is _____ .

9. The past tense of <u>fly</u> is _____ .

grew, drew, drank, hung, went, saw, found, sent, flew

Exercise 28.5
Fill in the vowel teams for the common long vowel sounds:

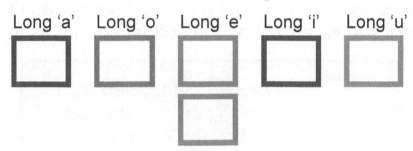

Long 'a'   Long 'o'   Long 'e'   Long 'i'   Long 'u'

ai, oa, ee & ea, ie, ue

Exercise 28.6
Choose the word that makes sense for each sentence:

stage	revenge	energy	change
edge	bridge	strangers	gentle

1. The sun makes solar _____.

2. The boy was _____ with the bird.

3. The actor walked up onto the _____.

4. Jim had to _____ the flat tire.

5. The new people were _____ in our town.

6. The angry girl said she will have _____.

7. The diver stood at the _____ of the cliff.

8. The town is just over the _____ .

Exercise 28.7
Do the dictations for this lesson at www.yourkidcanread.com.

Up to this point, 'c' has had a hard /k/ sound, as in "cat".
Now we'll see when 'c' has the soft /s/ sound, as in "city".

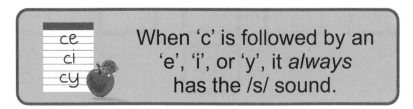

When 'c' is followed by an 'e', 'i', or 'y', it *always* has the /s/ sound.

dan<u>ce</u>   <u>ci</u>rcle   fan<u>cy</u>

ge gi gy } /j/	ce ci cy } /s/
sometimes	always

Read the following; each word has 'cent' = /sent/:

cent	percent	crescent	scent
recent	decent	accent	innocent

Read the following; each word has 'ace' = /ase/:

ace	grace	race
embrace	interlace	space
face	place	trace

Read the following; each word has 'ice' = /ise/:

advice	lice	nice	spice	twice
ice	mice	slice	splice	vice

Exercise 29.1
Read the clues and change the word so that it makes sense:

1. When water freezes it makes: rice   _____

2. Run fast so you can win the: rack   _____

3. Your nose is in the center of your: fact   _____

4. Sometimes you have to ask for: advise   _____

5. One time is once, two times is: nice   _____

6. A rocket ship goes into: spice   _____

ice, race, face, advice, twice, space

Exercise 29.2
Read the sentences and circle the words that makes sense:

1. We **recently / decent** went on a trip to New York City.

2. Pepper and salt are a type of **space / spice**.

3. Jim ate a **splice / slice** of pizza for lunch.

4. I had to **replace / embrace** the wiper blades on my car.

5. We have a fifty **cent / percent** chance of winning the game.

6. The judge ruled that the man was **recent / innocent**.

7. The opposite of mean is **twice / nice**.

8. The bad group of kids **faced / defaced** the statue.

9. My grandmother held me in an **embrace / interlace**.

---

* **Remember to break up large words**

magnificent

mag nif i cent

Read the following; each word ends with 'cy' = /see/:
Note that these words are difficult, so help out when needed, by covering the word with your finger and revealing a sound at a time.

accuracy	clemency	emergency	occupancy
adequacy	conspiracy	fallacy	policy
agency	currency	intimacy	potency
aristocracy	delicacy	juicy	pricy
bankruptcy	delinquency	latency	saucy
bouncy	democracy	lunacy	spicy
candidacy	dependency	mercy	transparency
chancy	dormancy	normalcy	vacancy

Exercise 29.3
Read the sentences and circle the words that makes sense:

1. The meal at the restaurant was rather **delicacy / pricy**.

2. It was the **policy / normalcy** of the theater to not allow food.

3. The model **agency / potency** was looking for new talent.

4. You must be calm in an **occupancy / emergency**.

5. The judge showed no **policy / mercy**.

6. Money is another word for **vacancy / currency**.

7. Our government is a **democracy / conspiracy**.

A Workbook for Dyslexics - Cheryl Orlassino   -136-

You may have noticed that many words do not follow the rules. For example, the word "model" does not double the 'd' to protect the short 'o'.

When reading, follow the rules, and then change the word to be a word that you know that makes sense.

Below are more sounds with 'ce' as /s/:

ance	ence	ince	once	unce

d<u>ance</u>   h<u>ence</u>   pr<u>ince</u>   sc<u>once</u>   d<u>unce</u>

Remember to put new sounds/rules on flash cards, and review every day until mastered.

Read the following:

advance	dance	hence	sentence
balance	distance	importance	sequence
chance	entrance	influence	silence
clearance	finance	instance	stance
commence	fragrance	occurrence	tolerance
convince	France	prince	trance

Below are more difficult words:

acceptance	appliance	hindrance	maintenance
acquaintance	compliance	independence	persistence
admittance	condolence	insurance	significance
affluence	conference	intelligence	
alliance	existence	intolerance	

Exercise 29.4

Circle the sounds that make a real word. There may be more than one correct answer for each line:

1. pl_____   ace   ice   ance   ince

2. ch_____   ace   ice   ance   ince

3. pr_____   ace   ice   ance   ince

4. gl_____   ace   ice   ance   ince

5. gr_____   ace   ice   ance   ince

6. sl_____   ace   ice   ance   ince

7. tr_____   ace   ice   ance   ince

8. sp_____   ace   ice   ance   ince

place, chance, price-prance-prince, glance, grace, slice, trace-trance, space-spice

Exercise 29.5

Read the sentences and circle the words that makes sense:

1. The spring clothes were on the **distance / clearance** rack.

2. Circle the word in the **sequence / sentence** that makes sense.

3. The seal tried to **influence / balance** the ball on his nose.

4. The **distance / importance** on the map was listed in miles.

5. The **prince / entrance** to the castle was by way of draw bridge.

6. I tried to **convince / distance** you to take a walk with me.

7. They took a **stance / chance** on hiring the lady.

Often, words with more than one syllable, ending with 'ice' and 'ace' have the /iss/, as in "kiss", sound:

notice   necklace

Read the following; note that all words end with the /iss/ sound:

accomplice	jaundice	menace	office
apprentice	justice	necklace	palace
crevice	lattice	notice	practice
hospice	malice	novice	service

Read the following mixed 'c' as /s/ words:

bounce	city	fleece	juice
announce	advice	pencil	lettuce
choice	force	farce	ounce
circle	Greece	flounce	voice

Exercise 29.6

Complete the words for the pictures below. Each one has a 'c' as /s/:

1.   lett _ _ _

4.   jui _ _

2.   neck _ _ _ _

5.   pen _ _ _

3.   just _ _ _

6.  b_ _ n_ _

Exercise 29.7

Read the sentences and choose the words that makes sense:

balance	face	center	race	choice
place	graceful	page	large	force

1. The snowball hit me in my _____.

2. The slowest runner came in last _____.

3. Jon slammed the door with a lot of _____.

4. The gymnast had to _____ on the rings.

5. Turn the _____ to see the next chapter.

6. The _____ woman could not fit in the dress.

7. My brother ran in a relay _____.

8. The _____ dancer leaped into the air.

9. We had a _____ to go to lunch or dinner.

10. The sun is the _____ of our solar system.

Exercise 29.8

Do the dictations for this lesson at www.yourkidcanread.com.

> * Remember to say the letter **sounds** as you
> write, *not* the letter names.

The /k/ Rule

In the last lesson, we saw that 'c' can have the /k/ sound, but it also has the /s/ sound, when it is followed by an 'e', 'i' or 'y'. Because of this, we have the /k/ rule:

When to use a 'c' or a 'k' for the /k/ sound.

When to Use 'c' or 'k'

Always use 'c' for the /k/ sound UNLESS:

1. the /k/ sound is followed by an 'e', 'i' or 'y', or
2. the /k/ sound is at the end of a one syllable word,

then you must use 'k'.

In the words below, /k/ is followed by 'e', 'i' or 'y', so we use 'k' for the /k/ sound:

<u>k</u>eep	<u>k</u>it	s<u>ky</u>
<u>k</u>ept	<u>k</u>ing	s<u>k</u>ip

If we used 'c', then we would not have /k/, we would have /s/ instead.

 kite ✓ **c**ite ✗

Some exceptions where the 'k' rule is not followed, are listed below:

s<u>k</u>ull   sk<u>u</u>nk   sk<u>a</u>te

Normally a 'c' would be used, since the vowel after the 'k' is NOT an 'e', 'i', or 'y'.

A Workbook for Dyslexics - Cheryl Orlassino   -141-

According to rule #2, we always use a 'k' at the end of a **one syllable** word ending with /k/.

du<u>k</u>   bri<u>k</u>   sta<u>k</u>   lu<u>k</u>

Two (or more) syllable words that
end with /k/ *usually* end with 'ic':

pan<u>ic</u>   top<u>ic</u>   traff<u>ic</u>   bas<u>ic</u>

Read the following:

allergic	classic	genetic	plastic	static
angelic	cosmic	ironic	public	terrific
attic	critic	Islamic	realistic	topic
basic	dyslexic	magic	robotic	toxic
civic	garlic	panic	romantic	traffic

There are some words that end with 'ic' that you have to
add a 'k' to when adding a suffix which starts with an 'e',
'i' or 'y' (like 'er', 'ed' and 'ing'):

picnic - picnic<u>ked</u> - picnic<u>ker</u> - picnic<u>king</u>

traffic - traffic<u>ked</u> - traffic<u>ker</u> - traffic<u>king</u>

panic - panic<u>ked</u> - panic<u>king</u>

If you didn't add the 'k', then the 'c' would change from a
/k/ sound to a /s/ sound.

Review; read the following:

agency	cease	civil	except	practice
balance	cell	clearance	excite	prance
cancel	chance	council	fancy	saucer
cancer	circle	dance	grace	science

Exercise 30.1

Use the 'k' rule to choose which letter (or letters) completes the word.

* The missing sound in all of these words is /k/ *

1. ___lam   (k, c)

2. s___orch   (k, c)

3. s ___in   (c, k)

4. ___ancel   (c, k)

5. lin____   (c, k)

6. cli____   (k, ck)

7. ___an   (k, c)

8. ___ounter (k, c)

9. picni___   (k, c)

10. ___it   (k, c)

11. ra___oon   (kk, cc)

12. hi___ups (kk, cc)

13. a___cent   (k, c)

14. ___eep   (k, c)

15. ___amping (k, c)

16. s___im   (k, c)

Answer key (left, upside down): counter, can, click, link, cancel, skin, scorch, clam

Answer key (right, upside down): skim, camping, keep, accent, hiccups, raccoon, kit, picnic

Exercise 30.2

Read the sentences to the student and have him/her fill in the following missing letters:

c	k	s

1. The boy used a **fa___e** finger to **s___are** the girl.

2. Our bodies have many **___ells**.

3. The man at the store tried to **___ell** me a new oven.

4. The little girl liked to **dan___e** around the room.

5. I will **dis___ard** the **jun___** mail.

6. There is a lot to do in the **___ity** on a **___unday**.

Answer key (upside down): fake, scare, cells, sell, dance, discard, junk, city, Sunday

Exercise 30.3
Choose the word that makes sense and write it on the line:

| traffic | plastic | mimic | frolic | tragic |
| logic | garlic | hectic | public | magic |

1. The busy day was very _____.

2. The boy did a _____ trick for us.

3. The cook chopped up the _____.

4. The toy was made of _____.

5. The puppy liked to _____ in the grass.

6. There was a lot of _____ on the highway.

7. The parrot likes to _____ people.

8. The _____ library was in the center of town.

9. Use _____ to solve the math problem.

10. The sad play had a _____ ending.

Exercise 30.4
Circle the words where a 'c' has the /s/ sound (there are 7):

cork	cube	plastic	slice
code	choice	crack	account
chance	place	canopy	accent
twice	embrace	collect	accumulate

accent
slice
embrace
place
choice
twice
chance

Exercise 30.5

Choose the word that makes sense and write it on the line:

wedge	cringed	garage	agent	pledge
plunge	dodge	gentle	ridged	aging

1. Please be _____ with the glass statue.

2. We keep our car in the _____ .

3. The skeleton makes the body_____ .

4. The _____ dog had trouble walking.

5. He stuck a _____ under the door to keep it open.

6. The secret _____ followed the suspect.

7. I took a _____ in the pool to cool off.

8. Every morning, we say the _____ of allegiance.

9. In gym class, we played _____ ball.

10. I _____ when the baseball landed near the baby.

Exercise 30.6

Circle the words where a 'g' has the /j/ sound (there are 3):

goat   grump   germ   gift

get   charge   anger   danger

charge, germ, danger

Exercise 30.7

Do the dictations for this lesson at www.yourkidcanread.com.

To make a noun plural (more than one),
there are some rules that you need to follow.
The same rules apply to make a verb singular.

Rules to Make a Noun Plural

1. If the word is irregular, use the irregular form:

   foot - feet   tooth - teeth   mouse - mice

2. If the word ends with /s/, /z/, /sh/, /ch/, or /x/, then add
   'es' to the word; note that you can **hear** this in the word.

   kiss - kiss<u>es</u>

   fizz - fizz<u>es</u>   batch - batch<u>es</u>

   box - box<u>es</u>

   bush - bush<u>es</u>

3. If the word ends with 'f' or 'fe', *usually* you take the 'f' or 'fe'
   out and add 'ves'; note that you can **hear** this in the word.

   loaf - loa<u>ves</u>   wife - wi<u>ves</u>

   * Some words can go either way:
   hoof - hoofs - hooves
   And some words are exceptions:
   roof - roofs

4. If the word ends with a consonant followed by a 'y', turn the
   'y' to an 'i' and add 'es'.

   cherry - cherr<u>ies</u>   memory - memor<u>ies</u>

5. If none of the above apply, you can just add an 's':

   hat - hat<u>s</u>   star - star<u>s</u>

Below is the decision tree for making a noun plural
(or a verb singular):

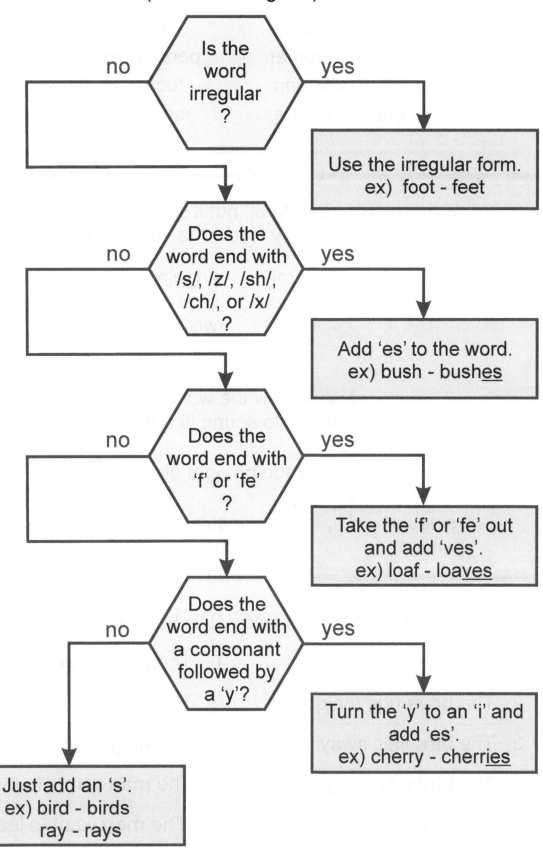

Is the word irregular ?

no → →

yes →

Use the irregular form.
ex) foot - feet

Does the word end with /s/, /z/, /sh/, /ch/, or /x/ ?

no →

yes →

Add 'es' to the word.
ex) bush - bush<u>es</u>

Does the word end with 'f' or 'fe' ?

no →

yes →

Take the 'f' or 'fe' out and add 'ves'.
ex) loaf - loa<u>ves</u>

Does the word end with a consonant followed by a 'y'?

no →

yes →

Turn the 'y' to an 'i' and add 'es'.
ex) cherry - cherr<u>ies</u>

Just add an 's'.
ex) bird - birds
ray - rays

Some Irregular Plural Nouns

man - men	foot - feet
woman - women	person - people
child - children	tooth - teeth
goose - geese	mouse - mice

Verbs can also be plural, but it's the **singular** verbs
that get the 's' - and they follow the same rules as nouns:

plural	singular
chase	chases
wish	wishes
say	says

Notice how the word "say"
changes to sound like /sez/.

The lady **<u>says</u>** to go right at the next corner.

singular ⟶   ⟵ singular verb
noun   (gets the 's' added)

Exercise 31.1
Underline the verb in each sentence. Note how the verbs change:

1. The **boy** <u>rides</u> his bike.

2. The **boys** <u>ride</u> their bikes.

3. The **bird** flies away.

4. The **birds** fly away.

5. The **girl** likes candy.

6. The **girls** like candy.

7. The **frog** lives on the pond.

8. The **frogs** live on the pond.

9. The **man** wants to leave.

10. The **men** want to leave.

Exercise 31.2
Write the words for the pictures below:

1.  _ _ _   _ _ _ _

2. _ _ _ _ _    _ _ _ _ _ _

3. _ _ _ _ _    _ _ _ _ _ _

4. _ _ _ _    _ _ _ _ _

5. _ _ _    _ _ _ _

6. _ _ _ _    _ _ _ _ _

7. _ _ _ _ _ _    _ _ _ _ _ _ _

8. _ _ _ _ _    _ _ _ _ _ _

9. _ _ _ _   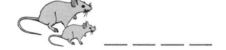 _ _ _ _

10. _ _ _ _ _    _ _ _ _ _ _

11. _ _ _ _ _ _    _ _ _ _ _ _ _

12. _ _ _ _ _    _ _ _ _ _

dog-dogs, baby-babies, watch-watches, loaf-loaves, box-boxes, wolf-wolves, cherry-cherries, scarf-scarves, mouse-mice, house-houses, cheese-cheeses, tooth-teeth

-149-

Read the following (singular nouns to plural nouns):

calf - calves	leaf - leaves	sheaf - sheaves
elf - elves	life - lives	thief - thieves
half - halves	loaf - loaves	wife - wives
hoof - hooves	scarf - scarves	wolf - wolves
knife - knives	self - selves	

house - houses	patch - patches	chance - chances
horse - horses	bush - bushes	* box - boxes
bus - busses	dish - dishes	* fox - foxes
buzz - buzzes	dance - dances	* tax - taxes

* Note how the 'x' is not doubled to protect the short vowel.

Read the following (plural verbs to singular verbs):

wish - wishes	carry - carries	fly - flies
rush - rushes	make - makes	spy - spies
bless - blesses	hurry - hurries	deny - denies
rest - rests	worry - worries	supply - supplies
think - thinks	study - studies	rectify - rectifies

Exercise 31.3
Circle the sounds that match the sounds on the left:

1.	oy	oa	oi	oe
2.	ew	oo	ee	ea
3.	igh	'i'	/g/	/ig/
4.	ce	/k/	/s/	ee
5.	ay	ee	ai	'i'
6.	aw	ai	oo	au

oy-oi, ew-oo, igh-'i', ce-/s/, ay-ai, aw-au

Exercise 31.4
Use the 'k' rule to choose which letter (or letters) completes the word.

* The missing sound in all of these words is /k/ *

1. __racker (k, c)
2. __onduct (k, c)
3. clini__ (c, k)
4. publi__ (c, k)
5. pani__ (c, k)
6. __iss (k, c)
7. __ick (k, c)
8. __actus (k, c)

9. __ake (k, c)
10. conta__t (k, c)
11. vi__tim (k, c)
12. for__ (k, c)
13. pitchfor__ (k, c)
14. __rack (k, c)
15. __ite (k, c)
16. havo__ (k, c)

cracker / conduct / clinic / public / panic / kiss / kick / cactus

cake / contact / victim / fork / pitchfork / crack / kite / havoc

Exercise 31.5
Circle the correct sound for the 'y' in each word:

1. cyst — long 'i' — short 'i' — long 'e'
2. symbolic — long 'i' — short 'i' — long 'e'
3. bicycle — long 'i' — short 'i' — long 'e'
4. pricy — long 'i' — short 'i' — long 'e'
5. cyber — long 'i' — short 'i' — long 'e'
6. fancy — long 'i' — short 'i' — long 'e'
7. agency — long 'i' — short 'i' — long 'e'
8. energy — long 'i' — short 'i' — long 'e'

1) short i, 2) short i, 3) short i, 4) long i, 5) long e, 6) long i, 7) long e, 8) long e

Exercise 31.6
Choose the word that makes sense and write it on the line:

announce	clearance	necklace	rancid
office	practice	service	convince

1. The restaurant had very bad _____ .

2. My mother works in an _____ .

3. The diamond _____ was worth millions.

4. The airplane had _____ to take off.

5. The lawyer tried to _____ the jury.

6. He needed a lot of _____ before his speech.

7. The principal will _____ the contest winner.

8. The spoiled food was _____ .

Exercise 31.7
Circle the correct way to make the noun plural or the verb singular:

1. hur**ry**   hurry**s** / hurr**ies**   5. par**ty**   party**s** / part**ies**

2. pu**sh**   push**s** / push**es**   6. crun**ch**   crunch**es** / crunch**s**

3. hal**f**   hal**ves** / half**s**   7. f**ry**   fr**ies** / fry**s**

4. ta**x**   tax**es** / tax**s**   8. sp**y**   spy**s** / sp**ies**

hurries, pushes, halves, taxes, parties, crunches, fries, spies

Exercise 31.8
Do the dictations for this lesson at www.yourkidcanread.com.

The word FLOSS is used to remind us to **double** the
'f', 'l' or 's' in words that: have one syllable, have a
short vowel, and ends with 'f', 'l' or 's'.

f̲ l̲ o s̲s̲

stu<u>ff</u>   hi<u>ll</u>   pa<u>ss</u>

Read the FLOSS words below:

double 'f'		double 'l'		double 's'	
cuff	cliff	tell	doll	glass	loss
stuff	huff	grill	hill	grass	mass
bluff	tiff	still	smell	miss	pass
scoff	stiff	dull	spill	fuss	toss

* Notice how all of the words above have:
one syllable
a **short** vowel
end in **'f', 'l', or 's'**

Exceptions: plus   bus   gas   yes

There are other one-syllable words with double 'l' that are not
considered FLOSS words, since the vowel 'o' is long:

r<u>oll</u>	poll	troll	volt	colt
toll	scroll	control	bolt	jolt

We also have one-syllable words with 'all', with the /awl/ sound:

all	fall	stall	hall	small
call	mall	wall	ball	tall

Exercise 32.1
Fill in the blanks to spell the FLOSS words for the pictures below:

1. sp __ __ __

2. dr __ __ __

3. b __ __ __

4. d __ __ __

5. sm __ __ __

6. dr __ __ __

7. p __ __ __

8. gr __ __ __

9. hand- c __ __ __ s

10. b __ __ __

spill, dress, boss, doll, smell,
drill, pill, grass, hand-cuffs, bell

Two Syllable Short Vowel Words

The FLOSS rule is only for **one syllable words**.

For **two or more syllable words** we sometimes double the last 's'. For this we have the following chant:

> Words ending with: less, ness,
> cess or tress,
> usually end with double 's'.

Read the following:

un<u>less</u>	fond<u>ness</u>	suc<u>cess</u>	dis<u>tress</u>
endless	happiness	access	fortress
careless	witness	recess	waitress
harmless	business	process	actress

Exercise 32.2
Circle the word that makes the most sense:

1. The judge called the **waitress / witness** up to the bench.

2. I prefer to sleep on a **fortress / mattress**.

3. The man was **harmless / careless**, and broke the vase.

4. If you work hard, you will find **distress / success**.

5. The large bees are usually **harmless / careless**.

6. Applying to college is a long **recess / process**.

7. The long, hot summer felt **endless / happiness**.

8. He was in the **process / business** of sales and marketing.

9. The stranded crew sent out a **harmless / distress** signal.

10. The **actress / waitress** served our meal.

Exercise 32.3
Circle the FLOSS words; remember FLOSS words are **one syllable** words, with **short** vowels ending with 'f', 'l' or 's' (there are 8):

off	spell	tell
will	grill	scoff
poll	roll	less
unless	toll	dull

off, will, spell, grill, tell, scoff, less, dull

Just like the 'o' is long in the words below (we saw these on the first page of this lesson), there are other words where 'o' is long for no reason:

r<u>o</u>ll	poll	troll	volt	colt
toll	scroll	control	bolt	jolt

In the four words below, 'ost' has the /oast/ sound, as in the word "roast":

p<u>o</u>st	m<u>o</u>st	h<u>o</u>st	gh<u>ost</u>

In the words below, 'old' has the sound as in "cold":

h<u>o</u>ld	f<u>o</u>ld	c<u>o</u>ld	g<u>o</u>ld
s<u>o</u>ld	f<u>o</u>lder	t<u>o</u>ld	b<u>o</u>ld

* Put all of the above words on flash cards for review.

Exercise 32.4
Draw lines to match the rhyming words:

1.	hold	pair
2.	lost	pole
3.	find	bowled
4.	care	kite
5.	sight	sigh
6.	most	blew
7.	roll	crossed
8.	clue	roast
9.	snow	lined
10.	try	toe

Exercise 32.5
Read each sentence and change the word so that it makes sense:

1. I _____ go swimming in the morning.
   most

2. The parents _____ a party for my grandmother.
   host

3. Last year, they _____ the old car.
   sell

4. The new mother will _____ her baby.
   held

5. Yesterday, I _____ my friend a secret.
   tell

6. The man _____ demanded to go first.
   bold

7. I _____ my comment on-line.
   post

8. The mean lady _____ looked at me and smiled.
   cold

9. My dog _____ out of the house.
   bolt

10. I was _____ my laundry when the door-bell rang.
    fold

mostly, hosted, sold, hold, told, boldly, posted, coldly, bolted, folding

Exercise 32.6
Circle the words that have a long 'o' (there are 9):

roll	boiler	most	follow	grow
doll	coldness	lost	pod	glow
dollar	scroll	sold	float	drop

glow, grow, float, follow, sold, most, scroll, coldness, roll

Exercise 32.7
Fill in the blanks to spell the words for the pictures below:

1. g _ _ _

2. scr _ _ _

3. f _ _ _ _ _

   gold, scroll, folder,
   ghost, bolt, roll

6. gh _ _ _

7. b _ _ _ _

8. r _ _ _

Exercise 32.8
Make the following words plural (if it's a noun) and singular (if it's a verb). In both cases, the word should end with an 's'.

1. waitress _____

2. witness _____

3. life _____

4. carry _____

5. marry _____

6. fly _____

7. memory_____

8. hurry _____

waitresses, witnesses, lives, carries, marries, flies, memories, hurries

Exercise 32.9
Write the **long vowel** sounds that are in the words below (the first one was done for you):

1. post [O]
2. blow [ ]
3. gold [ ]
4. tray [ ]

5. wild [ ]
6. mild [ ]
7. child [ ]
8. find [ ]

9. kind [ ]
10. fright [ ]
11. slow [ ]
12. hold [ ]

13. fry [ ]
14. scroll [ ]
15. they [ ]
16. roll [ ]

1) o, 2) o, 3) o, 4) a, 5) i, 6) i, 7) i, 8) i, 9) i, 10) i, 11) o, 12) o, 13) i, 14) o, 15) a 16) o

Exercise 32.10
Do the dictations for this lesson at www.yourkidcanread.com.

Large words, that have more than two syllables, can be intimidating. We already saw some large word in earlier lessons, and we will see more here. When you see a large word, you should do the following:

When reading a long word:

1. Identify which vowels are long or short.*

2. Identify the sounds you learned.

3. Break the word up into smaller pieces.

4. Sound it out, and change a bit, if needed, so it becomes a word you know that fits in the sentence.

* In multi-syllable words, the VCV rule isn't always followed.

In the word below, you may think the 'i's after the 'n' and after the 'f' are long (due to VCV), however, they are not. This often happens in large words.

significance

sig nif ic ance

---

delinquency

de lin qu en cy

In this word the 'n' has the same sound as the 'n' sound in the /nk/ words (such as "link"). This is because the qu has the /kw/ sound.

Sound the word out as you would normally do, then change it slightly so that it becomes a word you recognize.

In the word below, you may think the 'e' after the 'r' is long, however, it is not. Sound it out the with the rules you learned, and then changed the word so theat it becomes one you know.

prejudice

pre ju dice

Remember, words with two or more syllables that ends with 'ice' or 'ace' often end with the /iss/ sound.

---

maintenance

main ten ance

---

condolence

con dol ence

---

surprisingly

sur pris ing ly

* Remember, 's' can have the /z/ sound.

---

emroidery

em broid er y

Compound Words:

A compound word is when two words are combined to make one longer word.

When you join two words, you keep all of the letters that are in both original words, even though you may not need them.

ea<u>r</u> + <u>r</u>ing = ea<u>rr</u>ing

nigh<u>t</u> + <u>t</u>ime = nigh<u>tt</u>ime

Read the compound words below':

afternoon	footnote	newscaster	teaspoon
anybody	forbid	nighttime	themselves
anyhow	forget	nobody	thunderstorm
anymore	forklift	overboard	toolbox
anyone	grandmother	overflow	underage
backstage	graveyard	pancake	update
backtrack	haircut	popcorn	upgrade
backward	herself	postcard	wallpaper
became	himself	saucepan	waterfall
beforehand	hometown	scarecrow	wavelength
cannot	itself	software	weekday
caretaker	lifetime	somebody	weekend
driveway	limelight	someday	whatever
fireflies	mainland	sunflower	within
fireworks	meantime	taxpayer	without

Exercise 33.1

Choose the word that makes sense for each sentence below:

driveway	sunflower	upgrade	teaspoon
thunderstorm	mainland	meantime	caregiver
saucepan	backstage	haircut	toolbox

1. My dog hides under the bed during a _____ .

2. I like to add a _____ of sugar to my tea.

3. He went to the barber shop for a _____ .

4. We took a boat over to the _____ for supplies.

5. James parked the car on the _____ .

6. The actor was waiting _____ .

7. In the _____ , we ran to the store to get snacks.

8. They hired a _____ to help the sick lady.

9. Keep your hammer in the _____ .

10. We planted a _____ in the soil.

11. Fry the garlic in a small _____ .

12. I had to _____ the software on my computer.

A Workbook for Dyslexics - Cheryl Orlassino -162-

Exercise 33.2

Fill in the letters to complete the words so that the sentences make sense:

1. We **plan**__ __ __ to go out on Saturday night.

2. The peacock **fan**__ __ __ out his large tail.

3. He was **look**__ __ __ for his new pair of sneakers.

4. The boys were **sit**__ __ __ __ on the edge of the cliff.

5. The gardener **plant**__ __ a crop of lettuce.

6. The girl **slap**__ __ __ the horse on its rear-end.

Exercise 33.3

Fill in the letters to complete the words so that the sentences make sense:

1. What **happen**__ __ to the people in the car accident?

2. I was **listen**__ __ __ to the song while driving.

3. Jane **travel**__ __ to a different country.

4. I was outside, **garden**__ __ __ when the storm blew in.

5. The group of students were **permit**__ __ __ to see the show.

6. The parents **prefer**__ __ __ to watch the children.

7. The concert **benefit**__ __ __ the poor people.

8. The boy **pocket**__ __ the change.

9. She was **edit**__ __ __ her report before she handed it in.

10. We were **begin**__ __ __ __ to think he would not show up.

Remember, when adding a suffix (other than 'ing') to words that end with a consonant followed by a 'y', the 'y' turns to an 'i'. Sometimes, the 'i' will sound like a long 'e'.

Exercise 33.4
Add 'er to the words below:

1. garden _____   6. simple _____

2. run _____   7. large _____

3. fold _____   8. post _____

4. worry _____   9. party _____

5. sunny _____   10. hot _____

simpler, larger, poster, partier, hotter,
gardener, runner, folder, worrier, sunnier,

Exercise 33.5
Complete the words for each sentence below:

1. **Pl __ __ se** take the garbage to the curb. [ee , ea]

2. What **c __ __ sed** the tidal wave? [aw , au]

3. The soup had too much salt and tasted __ __ **ful**. [aw , au]

4. I had a **f __ __ ling** that he would be late. [ee , ea]

5. Jim did not **all __ __** himself to eat any cake. [ou , ow]

6. John could not **st __ __ r** the car and lost control. [ee , ea]

7. All he wanted was **p__ __ ce** and quiet. [ee , ea]

please, caused, awful, feeling, allow, steer, peace

Exercise 33.6
Do the dictations for this lesson at www.yourkidcanread.com.

A contraction is when two words are pushed together, and one or more letters gets popped out while an apostrophe gets pushed in. We already saw this with the word "we're":

we are = we're

Example:

you are = you're

An apostrophe is added where the letter (or letters) used to be. In the above example, the 'a' in the word "are" was popped out and replaced with an apostrophe.

Read the following contractions:

you're - you are	we've - we have	couldn't - could not
you've - you have	she'll - she will	shouldn't - should not
you'd - you would	he'll - he will	hasn't - has not
it's - it is	she's - she is	don't - do not
I'm - I am	he's - he is	doesn't - does not
they'll - they will	haven't - have not	didn't - did not
they're - they are	I'll - I will	that's - that is
they've - they have	wouldn't - would not	weren't - were not

Read the following:

1. She didn't have her homework in her backpack.
2. I wouldn't go to that part of town after dark.
3. They've been fighting all day.
4. I'm guessing that you didn't want the fish for dinner.
5. He's the only one who finished his project.
6. You'd think he was trying to impress the girl.
7. You shouldn't look directly into the sun.

Common Mistakes with Contractions

don't doesn't	"don't" is a contraction for "do not". I <u>don't</u> like to cook. "doesn't" is a contraction for "does not" He <u>doesn't</u> like to cook.
it's its	"it's" is a contraction for "it is". <u>It's</u> nice to see you. "its" is a personal pronoun. The snake shed <u>its</u> skin.
they're there	"they're" is a contraction for "they are". <u>They're</u> going to dinner. Use "there" to indicate a place. I'll be <u>there</u> after lunch.

Exercise 34.1
Draw a line to match the contractions with their partners:

1.	he's	does not
2.	it's	do not
3.	we've	could not
4.	haven't	should not
5.	didn't	did not
6.	they've	have not
7.	shouldn't	it is
8.	don't	he is
9.	doesn't	we have
10.	couldn't	they have

could not
does not
do not
should not
they have
did not
have not
we have
it is
he is

Exercise 34.2

Below are some FLOSS words that do **not** have the last letter doubled.
Read the words and circle the misspelled FLOSS words (there are 13):

fluf   bin   chil   cuf   dril

bet   vet   fil   cut   spil

wil   gues   bel   puf   pet

mis   stuf   pat   swel   pin

(answer key, upside down in left margin): spill, dril, swel, put, ou, bel, ill, chill, stuf, gues, mis, will, fluf

Exercise 34.3

Read the following sentences, and circle the words that make sense and **then** write the **contraction** on the line (the first one was done for you):

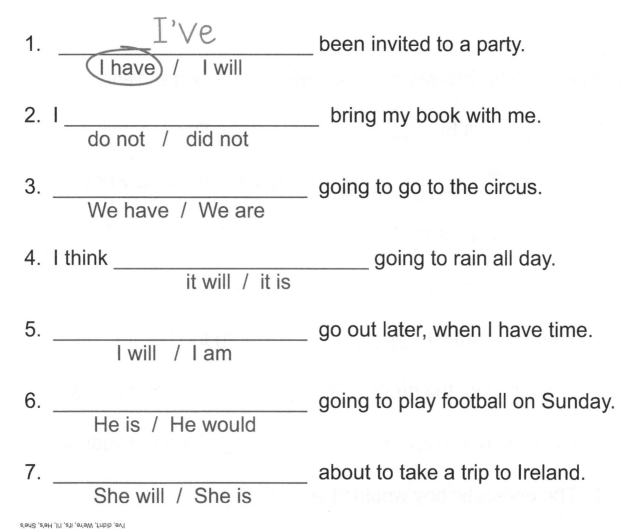

1. _____I've_____ been invited to a party.
   (I have) / I will

2. I _____ bring my book with me.
   do not / did not

3. _____ going to go to the circus.
   We have / We are

4. I think _____ going to rain all day.
   it will / it is

5. _____ go out later, when I have time.
   I will / I am

6. _____ going to play football on Sunday.
   He is / He would

7. _____ about to take a trip to Ireland.
   She will / She is

(answer key, upside down): I've, didn't, We're, it's, I'll, He's, She's

Exercise 34.4
Write the contracted form for the words on the lines:

1. I have _____

2. you would _____

3. you will _____

4. it is _____

5. they are _____

6. she is _____

7. I will _____

8. is not _____

9. they will _____

10. has not _____

11. does not _____

12. do not _____

I've, you'd, you'll, it's, they're, she's, I'll, isn't, they'll, hasn't, doesn't, don't

Exercise 34.5
Complete the FLOSS words that are missing for each sentence:

1. The girl likes to __sm_____ the flowers.

2. Use a __dr_____ to make a hole in the wood.

3. Jill studied a lot so that she'd __p_____ the test.

4. If you don't clean the garage, it'll be a __m_____.

5. There was an oil __sp_____ in the harbor.

6. In the spring, the green __gr_____ starts to grow.

7. I'd like to get a new __dr_____ for the wedding.

8. The energetic boy wouldn't sit __st_____.

spill, grass, dress, still
smell, drill, pass, mess,

Exercise 34.6
Circle the word where the 'ow' has the **long 'o'** sound:

1. tower / grow
2. flow / flower
3. shower / show
4. gown / slow
5. crow / crowd
6. stow / cower
7. mow / how

8. fellow / brow
9. allow / owner
10. shallow / clown
11. brown / borrow
12. low / crown
13. follow / town
14. powder / shadow

Exercise 34.7
Fill in the vowel teams for the common long vowel sounds:

Long 'a'	Long 'o'	Long 'e'	Long 'i'	Long 'u'

Exercise 34.8
Circle the sentence where the underlined word is correctly used:

It's body is large. / Its body is large.

He is over their. / He is over there.

He doesn't like cheese. / He don't like cheese.

Exercise 34.9
Do the dictations for this lesson at www.yourkidcanread.com.

A homophone is a word that sounds the same as another word, but is sometimes spelled differently and has a different meaning. The best way to learn these is to go over them and read a lot. You probably know many of the homophones listed below. Read through the list below and check off the ones you know:

buy, by, bye	hi, high	scene, seen
there, their, they're	whole, hole	seam, seem
to, too, two	new, knew	sew, so, sow
or, ore	it's, its	some, sum
our, hour	night, knight	son, sun
ate, eight*	lead*, led	steel, steal
blue, blew	maid, made	tale, tail
sent, cent, scent	one, won	sore, soar
course, coarse	passed, past	threw, through
dear, deer	peace, piece*	waist, waste
desert, dessert	plane, plain	wear, where
due, do, dew	pore, pour, poor	which, witch
die, dye	principal, principle	weather*, whether
hare, hair	road, rode, rowed	wait, weight*
here, hear	sea, see	wood, would
heard*, herd	read*, red	you're, your
air, heir*	right, rite, write	

* Note that some sounds/rules for some words above have not yet been covered. Just read those to your student, and tell him/her that we will talk about them in another lesson.

Common Mix Ups

to   too   two

I will go <u>to</u> the store.	A destination, or a point in time.
I like that song <u>too</u>. I have <u>too</u> many things.	Means "also" or "many" hint: too many 'o's
I have <u>two</u> dogs.	The number 2.

their   there   they're

<u>Their</u> house is brown.	Belongs to someone or something.
I will go <u>there</u> later.	Indicates a place.
<u>They're</u> going home.	A contraction for "they are".

Spelling Hint

The word "the" is in:

<u>the</u>ir, <u>the</u>re and <u>the</u>y're

Related Words:
here there where
Each of these words has the word "here" in them, and they all relate to each other.
<u>Where</u> are you? I'm <u>here</u>? Are you <u>there</u>?

Exercise 35.1
Circle the correct word for the sentence:

1. The (scent , cent , sent) of the perfume was strong.

2. The (dear , deer) crossed the (road , rode).

3. I will have apple pie for (desert , dessert).

4. The dog's (tale , tail) wagged when he greeted the children.

5. My mother needs to (dye , die) her (hair , hare).

6. The dog chased the (hair , hare) through the woods.

7. Of (course , coarse) you look good in that dress!

8. How (high , hi) can a balloon float?

9. The (whole , hole) in my pocket was in the (seam , seem).

10. I will need to (sew , so, sow) the pocket when I get home.

scent, deer, road, dessert, tail, dye, hair,
hare, course, high, hole, seam, sew

* Since your student probably has not been exposed to the spelling of homophones, this may be new to him or her. If this is the case, have him/her take a good guess, and then explain the meaning of the word(s).

Exercise 35.2
Circle the word that answers the question:

1. Which word means "also" or "many"?   to   too   two

2. Which word means "a place"?   their   there   they're

3. Which word means "they are"?   their   there   they're

4. Which word means "a direction"?   to   too   two

5. Which word means "ownership"?   their   there   they're

too, there, they're, to, their

> Related Words:
>
> some
> come
>
> In these words, the 'ome' has the /um/ sound.
>
> some = /sum/ & come = /cum/

Exercise 35.3

Circle the words that complete the sentences:

1. Frank wants to go **there / their** with his girlfriend.

2. What are **some / sum** of your ideas?

3. Come here and tell me what you **wood / would** do.

4. The horse ran the race and **one / won**.

5. We went **too / to / two** the store to **buy / bye / by** food.

6. **There / Their** house was on fire.

7. After dinner, we ate our **desert / dessert**.

8. The girl **road / rode** her horse down the street.

9. The wind **blue / blew** the door open.

10. She ran right **passed / past** me.

11. I **passed / past** the test.

12. The **deer / dear** ran into the woods.

there, some, would, won, to, buy, Their,
dessert, rode, blew, past, passed, deer

> To help remember "dessert" and "desert":
> "dessert" has to 's's - for two <u>s</u>coops of ice-cream.

Exercise 35.4
Circle the correct word that corresponds to the given meaning:

1. Hamburger is made of __?__.
   meet / meat

2. To purchase something.
   bye / buy / by

3. Opposite of rich.
   pore / poor / pour

4. You use your eyes to __?__.
   sea / see

5. You use your ears __?__.
   here / hear

6. One penny is a __?__.
   cent / sent

7. First, second, third, __?__.
   forth / fourth

8. You get this from a tree.
   wood / would

9. The past tense of "throw".
   through / threw

10. The opposite of "low".
    hi / high

meat, buy, poor, see, hear,
cent, fourth, wood, threw, high

Exercise 35.5
Circle the correct word for each sentence:

1. I cannot find **were / where / we're** his house is on the map.

2. What **were / where / we're** they going to do at the park?

3. I like **were / where / we're** they plan to have the party.

4. **Were / Where / We're** going to go to the beach on Saturday.

5. My sisters **were / where / we're** supposed to meet me.

6. I think **were / where / we're** going to see the show later.

where, were, where, We're, were, we're

Exercise 35.6
Do the dictations for this lesson at www.yourkidcanread.com.

Lesson 36

Words with 'wh' and Silent Letters

In many words there are silent letters. There are no rules to follow, you simply must familiarize yourself with these words and learn how to spell them.

Words with silent 'b': *(Note, underlined vowels are long.)*

debt	dumb	plumber	climb
doubt	numb	tomb	bomb
crumb	thumb	lamb	comb

Words with silent 'k':

knee	knew	knife	knit
kneel	known	knight	knob
know	knuckle	knot	knock

Words with silent 'w':

answer	two	wrap	wrist
sword	write	wrong	wrinkle
toward	wrote	wreck	wretch

Words with silent 'n':

autumn   column   condemn   hymn   solemn

Words with silent 's':

island   aisle   debris   Arkansas   Illinois

Words with silent 'h':

hour	honor	heir	rhyme
herb	honest	ghost	rhythm

There are many letter
combinations with silent 'g's.

Below are words where you do not hear the 'g':

campaign	feign*	gnarl	gnat	gnome
diaphragm*	foreign*	gnash	gnaw	straight

Some sounds have not yet been covered. Read these to your student.

The following are words that have 'gh' combined with other letters
to get some different sounds, such as long 'o' and /oo/ as in "boo":

through	dough	though	thorough

In the following words, 'ign' has the /ine/ sound:

align   sign   design   resign

As seen in an earlier lesson, 'igh' can have the long 'i' sound:

high	right	bright	flight	night
sigh	might	fight	plight	light

* Words like "caught", "cough", "bought" and "weigh"
will be covered in later lessons.

Exercise 36.1
For each sentence, choose the word that fits and write it on the line:

aisle	toward	write	knot
two	answer	knight	know

1. The _____ in shining armor came to my rescue.

2. Please_____my question.

3. Do you _____ how to get there?

4. The boy scout tied a _____ in the rope.

5. The bride walked up the _____.

6. I ducked as the bird flew _____ me.

7. My friend has _____ boys in her family.

8. I will _____ you a letter when I get there.

Exercise 36.2
Circle the word that makes the most sense:

1. I wish I had **know / known** that you would be there.

2. **Wrap / Write** the baby in a blanket.

3. The old lady **new / knew** about the secret room.

4. Did you hear a **knot / knock** at the door?

5. The man got down on one **kneel / knee** to propose.

7. Use a sharp **knife / knit** to cut the rope.

Exercise 36.3
Circle the word that makes the most sense:

1. We had to **knee / kneel** in the church.

2. The answer wasn't right, it was **toward / wrong**.

3. Did you get the letter that I **write / wrote** you?

4. Turn the **knot / knob** to open the door.

5. The old lady liked to **wreck / knit** blankets for the babies.

6. List the items in one **column / island**.

7. My cotton shirt had a lot of **crumbs / wrinkles**.

8. The crew was stranded on a deserted **island / autumn**.

9. If you spend too much money, you will be in **wrong / debt**.

Exercise 36.4
Match the words that are homophones (words that sound the same, but have different meanings):

1.	knight	site
2.	write	hole
3.	sight	new
4.	no	night
5.	hi	know
6.	hour	right
7.	knew	high
8.	whole	our

knight-night
write-right
sight-site
no-know
hi-high
hour-our
knew-new
whole-hole

Words with 'wh'

In words that start with 'wh', we *usually* pronounce the word with a silent 'h'. However, technically, these words are supposed to be pronounced with a /w/ sound with air passing through.

what	where	which	whale	white
when	why	while	wheel	whether

who = /hoo/

To help remember some of the common 'wh' words, think of "newspaper words". These are the words that journalists must answer when writing an article:

who   what   when   where   why   (and how)

Exercise 36.5

Fill in the missing silent letters (letters in the box can be used more than once):

b   k   n   h   s

1. de__t
2. __now
3. __nock
4. autum__
5. i__land

6. dou__t
7. __our
8. crum__
9. __onor
10. __nuckle

11. __not
12. dum__
13. thum__
14. bom__
15. num__

Exercise 36.6
Fill in the letters to make the words for the pictures below:

1. _ _ _ _ _

2. _ _ _ _ _

3. _ _ _ _ _

4. _ _ _ _ _ _

5. _ _ _ _ _ _ le

6. s _ _ _ _

7. _ _ _ _ _ _

8.  _ _ _ _ _

9.  _ _ _ _ _

10. _ _ _ _

11. _ _ _ _ _ _

12. _ _ _ _ _

13. _ _ _ _

14. l _ _ _

knee, thumb, knife, autumn, whistle, sword, island, ghost, whale, bomb, knight, wheel, knob, lamb

Exercise 36.7
Circle the word that is spelled correctly:

1. who / hoo   4. rong / wrong

2. wrinkle / rinkle   5. toard / toward

3. anser / answer   6. climb / clime

who, wrinkle, answer, wrong, toward, climb

Exercise 36.8
Do the dictations for this lesson at www.yourkidcanread.com.

When we learned about long vowels, we learned that when two vowels are together, the first vowel becomes long, and the second vowel is usually silent (but not always).

In this lesson, and the next lesson, we are going to break that rule with vowel teams that make different sounds.

 We call these vowel teams "rule breakers".

'ei' *sometimes* makes the long 'a' sound.

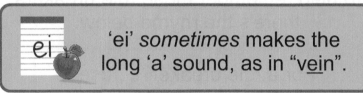

'ei' *sometimes* makes the long 'a' sound, as in "v<u>ei</u>n".

w<u>ei</u>gh	fr<u>ei</u>ght	f<u>ei</u>gn	n<u>ei</u>gh
w<u>ei</u>ght	n<u>ei</u>ghbor	v<u>ei</u>n	sl<u>ei</u>gh
<u>ei</u>ght	b<u>ei</u>ge	h<u>ei</u>r	

* Many of these words have a silent 'gh' in them:

'ie *sometimes* makes the long 'e' sound.

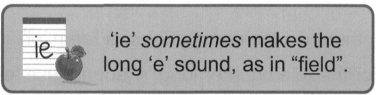

'ie' *sometimes* makes the long 'e' sound, as in "f<u>ie</u>ld".

* In this case, the **second** vowel does the talking.

ach<u>ie</u>ve	f<u>ie</u>ld	rel<u>ie</u>f	retr<u>ie</u>ver
bel<u>ie</u>ve	gr<u>ie</u>f	rel<u>ie</u>ve	ser<u>ie</u>s
br<u>ie</u>f	gr<u>ie</u>ve	repr<u>ie</u>ve	sh<u>ie</u>ld
ch<u>ie</u>f	p<u>ie</u>ce	retr<u>ie</u>ve	y<u>ie</u>ld

'y' and 'ie' are BOTH used to make the
long 'e' sound at the end of a word:

Aunt<u>ie</u>	coll<u>ie</u>	gen<u>ie</u>	mean<u>ie</u>
Aussie	cookie	goalie	oldie
biggie	cutie	goldie	sweetie
blankie	dearie	goodie	zombie
boogie	Dixie	indie	
brownie	doggie	kiddie	
calorie	freebie	leftie	

To help remember these rule breakers,
there's the rhyme below:

> For a rule breaker 'e', use 'i'
> before 'e', except after 'c'
> and in words that have /ay/,
> like "n<u>ei</u>ghbor" and "w<u>ei</u>gh".

Let's look at the rhyme more in depth:

'i' before 'e' means:
For the (rule breaker) long 'e' sound, use 'ie'.

But if there is a 'c' *before* the 'e' sound,
then use the common vowel team 'ei'.

For the rule breaker long 'a' sound, use 'ei'
(the opposite of 'i' before 'e').

Below are examples of 'cei' words ('cei' = /see/):

<u>cei</u>ling	con<u>cei</u>t	de<u>cei</u>t	re<u>cei</u>pt
per<u>cei</u>ve	de<u>cei</u>ve	trans<u>cei</u>ver	re<u>cei</u>ve

Here's our new chart (the rule breakers are boxed in red):

Long 'a'	Long 'o'	Long 'e'	Long 'i'	Long 'u'
ai	oa	ee	ie	ue
ei		ea		
		ie		

Read the following:

1. The fire chief was the first one on the fire engine.
2. The soccer team ran out onto the field.
3. There was a brief pause before he spoke.
4. Our neighbor watched our pets when we went away.
5. When I went to the doctor, they used a scale to weigh me.

Exercise 37.1

Fill in the blanks with the correct letters to complete the words:

1.  sh__ __ __ __

2. c__ __k__ __

3. gen__ __

4. mov__ __

5. h__ __d__ __

6. d__ gg__ __

7. __ __ght

8. br__ __n__ __

9. b__ __t__ __

10. b__ __d__ __

shield, cookie, genie, movie, hoodie, doggie, eight, brownie, bootie, birdie

Exercise 37.2
Identify the sound that is underlined:

1.	br<u>igh</u>t	long ____	8.	cook<u>ie</u>	long ____
2.	m<u>igh</u>t	long ____	9.	<u>ei</u>ght	long ____
3.	str<u>ay</u>	long ____	10.	f<u>ie</u>ld	long ____
4.	repl<u>y</u>	long ____	11.	w<u>i</u>ld	long ____
5.	satisf<u>y</u>	long ____	12.	br<u>ie</u>f	long ____
6.	funn<u>y</u>	long ____	13.	ch<u>i</u>ld	long ____
7.	recentl<u>y</u>	long ____	14.	brown<u>ie</u>	long ____

Exercise 37.3
Circle the words that are spelled correctly:

1.	who / hoo	7.	brief / breaf
2.	clime / climb	8.	cooky / cookie
3.	feeld / field	9.	releef / relief
4.	eight / aight	10.	keep / keap
5.	deep / deap	11.	beleef / belief
6.	naybor / neighbor	12.	thum / thumb

Exercise 37.4
Fill in the missing silent letters:

1. __rist   3. ans__er   5. __nee   7. __rite

2. to__ard   4. num__   6. __rap   8. __nock

Lesson 37 - Double Vowel Rule Breakers, 'ei' and 'ie'

Exercise 37.5
Change the contractions to their un-contracted form:

1. doesn't _____ 5. she'll _____

2. haven't _____ 6. he's _____

3. wouldn't _____ 7. he'll _____

4. shouldn't _____ 8. don't _____

does not, have not, would not, should not, she will, he is, he will, do not

Exercise 37.6
Add the 'ing' suffix to the words:

1. carry _____ 5. split _____

2. study _____ 6. make _____

3. sleep _____ 7. take _____

4. identify _____ 8. pat _____

carrying, studying, sleeping, identifying, splitting, making, taking, patting

Exercise 37.7
Add the 'er' suffix to the words:

1. happy _____ 4. supply _____

2. carry _____ 5. funny _____

3. merry _____ 6. sleepy _____

happier, carrier, merrier, supplier, funnier, sleeper

Exercise 37.8
Do the dictations for this lesson at www.yourkidcanread.com.

A Workbook for Dyslexics - Cheryl Orlassino   -185-   Copyrighted material; not to be copied or distributed.

In the last lesson we saw the double vowel rule breakers: 'ie' and 'ei'. Remember, these rule breakers do NOT follow the rule: When two vowels go walking the first one does the talking.

Now we have two more double vowel rule breakers: 'ea' and 'ai'.

 'ea' and 'ai' Rule Breakers

'ea' *sometimes* makes the short 'e' sound.

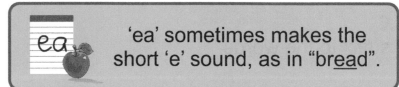

'ea' sometimes makes the short 'e' sound, as in "br<u>ea</u>d".

Read the words below (remember, 'ea' has the short 'e' sound):

ahead	feather	measure*	sweat
already	head	ocean	thread
bread	health	pageant	threat
breakfast	healthy	pleasant	treachery
breast	heaven	pleasure	tread
breath	heavy	read	treasure*
cleanser	instead	ready	wealth
dead	jealous	realm	wealthy
deaf	lead	sergeant	weapon
death	leapt	spread	weather
dread	leather	stead	
dreamt	meadow	steadfast	
endeavor	meant	steady	

* 'sure' = /shur/

Exercise 38.1

Complete the words below. Use 'ea' for the short 'e' sound:

1. m__ __sure

2. tr__ __sure

3. f__ __ __ __ __ers

4. w__ __pons

5. br__ __ __

6. thr__ __ __

7. h__ __vy

8. h__ __v__ __

9. sw__ __ t __ __

10. w__ __lth__

11. h__ __ __

12. w__ __th__ __

measure, treasure, feathers, weapons, bread, thread, heavy, heaven, sweater, wealthy, head, weather

---

 When reading, if letter pairs have more than one sound, try each sound and see which one makes sense.

He <u>read</u> the book.

I have to <u>read</u> the book.

Not only does 'ea' have a short 'e' sound, but,
in eight words, it has the long 'a' sound.

'ea' makes the long 'a' sound in only eight words.

 In eight words, 'ea' has the
long 'a' sound, as in "gr__ea__t".

Read the EIGHT words below, where 'ea' has the long 'a' sound:

1. br__ea__k   4. b__ea__r   7. t__ea__r
2. st__ea__k   5. p__ea__r   8. w__ea__r
3. gr__ea__t   6. sw__ea__r

Exercise 38.2
Complete the words below. Use 'ea' for the long 'a' sound:

1. p_ _ _

2. st_ _ _

3. b_ _ _

4. t_ _ _

pear, steak, bear, tear

 'ea' Review

'ea' can be a **long 'e'**, as in: beach

'ea' can be a **short 'e'**, as in: bread

'ea' can be a **long 'a'**, as in: pear
(in 8 words only)

Our last rule breaker is 'ai', which has the short 'e' sound.

In a few words, 'ai' makes the short 'e' sound.

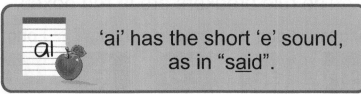

'ai' has the short 'e' sound, as in "s<u>ai</u>d".

Read the words below (remember, 'ai' has the short 'e' sound):

ag<u>ai</u>n	capt<u>ai</u>n	curt<u>ai</u>n
ag<u>ai</u>nst	cert<u>ai</u>n	fount<u>ai</u>n
barg<u>ai</u>n	chapl<u>ai</u>n	mount<u>ai</u>n
Brit<u>ai</u>n	chieft<u>ai</u>n	s<u>ai</u>d

When **spelling** words that do NOT sound the way they're spelled, you can try **saying** the word the way it **is** spelled (following the sounds and rules that you've learned).

For example:

mount<u>ai</u>n

When spelling this word, say this as if the 'ai' is a normal vowel team having the long 'a' sound.

 'ai' Review

'ai' can be a **long 'a'**, as in: p<u>ai</u>l

'ai' can be a **short 'e'**, as in: fount<u>ai</u>n

Below is our NEW long vowel chart, which shows most of the ways to get a **long** vowel sound, not including VCV:

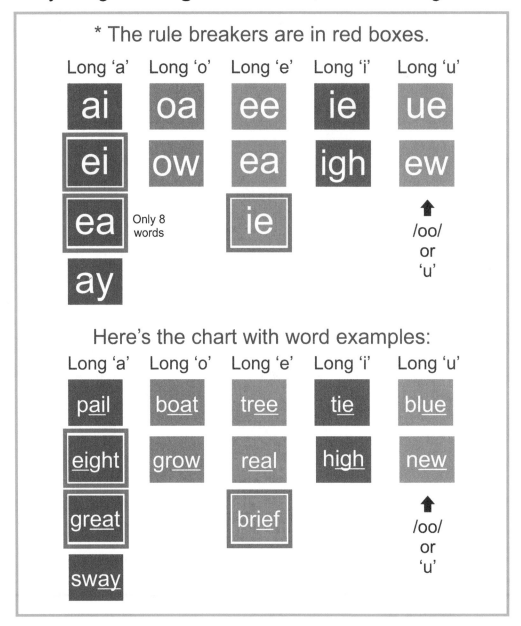

Exercise 38.3
Circle the words that are spelled correctly:

1. bred / bread
2. said / sed
3. health / helth
4. head / hed
5. agen / again
6. mounten / mountain
7. ready / reddy
8. certen / certain

bread, said, health, head, again, mountain, ready, certain

Exercise 38.4
Complete the words below. Use 'ai' for the short 'e' sound:

1. Br___ ___ ___ ___ ___

3. cap___ ___ ___ ___

2. f___ ___nt___ ___n

4. m___ ___nt___ ___n

5. cur___ ___ ___ ___

Britain, fountain, captain, mountain, curtain

Exercise 38.5
Write the answers to the questions below:

1. What is the rule breaker that makes the short 'e' sound as in:

 ___ ___

2. What is the rule breaker that makes the short 'e' sound as in:

 ___ ___

3. What is the rule breaker that makes the long 'a' sound as in:

8 ___ ___

4. What is the rule breaker that makes the long 'e' sound as in:

 ___ ___

ea, ai, ei, ie

Exercise 38.6
Draw lines to match the rhyming words:

1.	brief		said
2.	fled		leaf
3.	pear		air
4.	plate		heat
5.	went		bet
6.	sweet		meant
7.	sweat		eight

brief-leaf, fled-said, pear-air, plate-eight, went-meant, sweet-heat, sweat-bet

Exercise 38.7
Fill in the chart with the missing rule breakers:

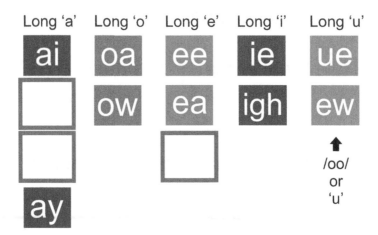

Long 'a'	Long 'o'	Long 'e'	Long 'i'	Long 'u'
ai	oa	ee	ie	ue
	ow	ea	igh	ew
				↑ /oo/ or 'u'
ay				

Exercise 38.8
Circle the rhyming words (there are two for each line):

1.	field	sealed	tied	5.	cry	sigh	fight
2.	beef	life	brief	6.	beak	take	break
3.	leader	leather	weather	7.	bear	hear	care
4.	right	eight	great	8.	cried	yield	healed

field-sealed, beef-brief, leather-weather, eight-great, cry-sigh, take-break, bear-care, yield-healed

Exercise 38.9

Circle the word that makes sense:

1. The soccer player **passed / past** the ball to the other player.

2. I thought I **heard / herd** a noise outside.

3. She **poured / pored** the milk into the cup.

4. The house is **buy / by / bye** the **sea / see**.

5. The boy **new / knew** how to boil the noodles for dinner.

6. **It's / Its** a **knew / new** car on the driveway.

7. **Your / You're** dog is sitting on my foot!

8. The boy **blew / blue** out the candles on his birthday cake.

9. The world's largest producer of iron **ore / oar / or** is in Brazil.

10. She **new / knew** he was going to cancel the appointment.

11. The **scene / seen** in the dark alley was scary.

12. If you add two numbers, you get the **sum / some**.

13. The **steel / steal** metal was cold to the touch.

14. The eagle will spread its wings and soar **threw / through** the air.

15. If we run out of juice, I will have to **buy / by / bye** more.

16. The kite flew **hi / high** up in the sky.

17. Some say you should wait an **our / hour** to swim after eating.

18. The sandpaper was **course / coarse** and bumpy.

Exercise 38.10

Do the dictations for this lesson at www.yourkidcanread.com.

Both 'tial' & 'cial' make the /shuhl/ sound.

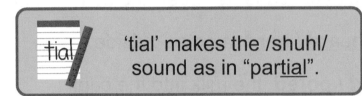

'tial' makes the /shuhl/ sound as in "par**tial**".

par**tial**   spa**tial**   mar**tial**

Read the words below (for '**i**tial', the first 'i' is short):

celestial	exponential	partial
circumstantial	influential	prudential
confidential	initial	residential
credential	initially	sequential
essential	martial	spatial
evidential	nuptial	substantial

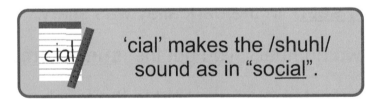

'cial' makes the /shuhl/ sound as in "so**cial**".

so**cial**   spe**cial**   fa**cial**

Read the words below (for '**i**cial', the first 'i' is short):

artificial	financial	racial
beneficial	glacial	sacrificial
commercial	judicial	superficial
crucial	multiracial	social
especially	official	spacial
facial	provincial	special

Read the following sentences:

1. The artificial sweetener is not good for you.
2. He especially liked the roller-coaster.
3. The president of the company sent an official letter to me.
4. It is crucial that you see a doctor if you are very sick.
5. Financially, we may be able to afford a new house.
6. Exercising is beneficial for your good health.
7. The boy studied the martial arts.
8. He lost a substantial amount of money at the horse race.
9. It is essential that you talk to the teacher about the problem.
10. The commercial advertised a new kind of soap.

When spelling a word that ends with the /shahl/ sound:

Usually '**tial**' follows a **consonant**.
Usually '**cial**' follows a **verb**.

(c)tial
(v)cial

par<u>tial</u>   spe<u>cial</u>

↑   ↑
consonant   noun

Exercise 39.1
Fill in the blank with: **cial**   or   **tial**

1. fa___ ___ ___ ___

2. cru___ ___ ___ ___

3. substan___ ___ ___ ___

4. essen___ ___ ___ ___

5. confiden___ ___ ___ ___

6. par___ ___ ___ ___

7. mar___ ___ ___ ___

8. benefi___ ___ ___ ___

facial, crucial, substantial, essential, confidential, partial, martial, commercial

---

Exercise 39.2
Circle the word that makes the most sense:

1. Dogs are **social / crucial** animals who live in packs.

2. Our class is **residential / multiracial**; there are many people from different backgrounds and countries.

3. On my birthday, I feel very **partial / special**.

4. The **credential / commercial** advertised a new toothpaste.

5. He received a **crucial / substantial** amount of money.

6. My backyard is **partially / especially** woods.

7. We live in a **crucial / residential** neighborhood.

8. I **especially / socially** love ice-cream with chocolate fudge.

9. They asked for his **socials / credentials** before hiring him.

10. It is **crucial / special** that you turn the gas off before leaving.

Exercise 39.3
Circle the sound for the letters that are underlined:

1. rel<u>ie</u>f	long 'e'	long 'i'	7. bel<u>ie</u>ve	long 'e'	long 'i'
2. d<u>ie</u>d	long 'e'	long 'i'	8. rec<u>ei</u>ve	long 'e'	long 'i'
3. spr<u>ea</u>d	long 'e'	short 'e'	9. l<u>ea</u>ve	long 'e'	short 'e'
4. sw<u>ee</u>t	long 'e'	short 'e'	10. br<u>ea</u>d	long 'e'	short 'e'
5. sw<u>ea</u>t	long 'e'	short 'e'	11. h<u>ea</u>d	long 'e'	short 'e'
6. gr<u>ea</u>t	long 'a'	long 'e'	12. ch<u>i</u>ld	long 'i'	short 'i'

long e, long i, short e, long e, short e, long e, short e, long e, long i, long e, short e, long i

Exercise 39.4
Choose the word that makes sense:

freight	neighbor	eight	weighs
sleigh	briefly	relief	vein

1. The new born baby _____ nine pounds.

2. My next door _____ always borrows my ladder.

3. I like to go _____ riding in the winter.

4. The nurse put the needle into the _____ in his arm.

5. The _____ train ran through town.

6. It was a _____ when the miners made it to safety.

7. All _____ puppies were healthy.

8. He spoke _____ to the crowd of people.

Exercise 39.5
Circle the word that is spelled correctly:

1. The opposite of strong is **week / weak**.

2. The homework for our class **seems / seams   eesy / easy**.

3. There was a **leek / leak** in the roof.

4. We **keep / keap** our food in the refidgerator.

5. The boy's room is very **neet / neat**.

6. The other side of the pool is the **deep / deap** side.

7. What is the **meening / meaning** of the word?

weak, easy, leak, keep, neat, deep, meaning

-197-

Exercise 39.6

Write the past tense form for the words below. Use the sentence below to help:

Today I _____, but yesterday I _____.

1. charge _____
2. change _____
3. place _____
4. hug _____
5. hurry _____

6. accept _____
7. balance _____
8. advance _____
9. rage _____
10. manage _____

charged, changed, placed, hugged, hurried, accepted, balanced, advanced, raged, managed

Exercise 39.7

Write the correct word on the line: **there their they're**

1. Once upon a time _____ was a princess.

2. I think _____ house is bigger than ours.

3. Suddenly, _____ was a loud crash!

4. I didn't know he would be _____ too.

5. I think _____ going to run in the race.

6. The boys were ready, but _____ mothers weren't.

7. _____ accepting new applicants for the job.

there, their, there, they're, their, they're

Exercise 39.8

Do the dictations for this lesson at www.yourkidcanread.com.

Both 'tion' & 'sion' make the /shun/ sound.

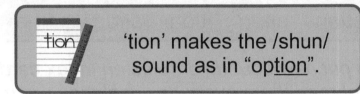

'tion' makes the /shun/ sound as in "op<u>tion</u>".

op<u>tion</u>   por<u>tion</u>   frac<u>tion</u>

Read the words below:

abduction	defection	infection
action	deflection	infliction
addiction	diction	intersection
affection	dictionary	junction
affliction	direction	objection
auction	ejection	obstruction
collection	eviction	perfection
conjunction	extraction	projection
constriction	faction	reaction
contraction	fiction	reflection
convection	fraction	restriction
deduction	function	section

adaption	consumption	eruption
adoption	contraception	inscription
absorption	corruption	option
caption	decryption	subscription
conception	disruption	transcription

assertion	distortion	extortion
desertion	exertion	portion

'tion' **after** a vowel

ALL vowels are long EXCEPT the 'i' in 'ition':

ation	etion	ition	otion	ution

Remember to put new sounds or rules on index cards and have your student read them every day until they are mastered.

Read the 'ation' words below:

celebration	population	accusation
nation	circulation	admiration
creation	civilization	location
vacation	transportation	imitation

Read the 'etion' words below:

deletion	completion
depletion	excretion

Read the 'ition' words below:

addition	ignition	condition
ambition	nutrition	definition
audition	edition	

Read the 'otion' words below:

commotion	lotion	potion
devotion	locomotion	promotion
emotion	notion	motion

Read the 'ution' words below:

contribution	institution	resolution
dilution	pollution	solution
execution	prosecution	substitution

Exercise 40.1
Circle the word that goes with the sentence:

1. Angry, happy, and sad are:

    motions   locations   emotions

2. When you solve a problem, you find the:

    subtraction   addition   solution

3. Use a dictionary to look up the:

    definition   edition   substitution

4. Burning junk causes:

    population   pollution   creation

5. For a birthday, marriage, or graduation, we have a:

    promotion   commotion   celebration

6. To take a child into your family as your own:

    eviction   adaption   adoption

7. The two roads cross at the:

    infection   intersection   obstruction

8. When you look into a mirror, you see your:

    reflection   projection   distortion

9. When you have more than one choice, you have an:

    reaction   auction   option

10. Words like "they're", "don't", and "haven't" are:

    fractions   sections   contractions

11. To be perfect in all respects:

    perfection   distortion   commotion

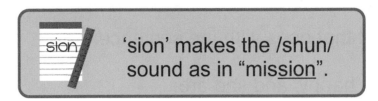

'sion' makes the /shun/ sound as in "mis**sion**".

mis**sion**   ses**sion**   impres**sion**

Read the words below:

admission	expression	possession
aggression	expansion	procession
commission	impassion	profession
compassion	impression	progression
compression	intermission	recession
concussion	mansion	regression
confession	omission	session
depression	passion	submission
discussion	percussion	transgression
emission	permission	transmission

Exercise 40.2

Circle the word that makes the most sense:

1. The wealthy man lives in a **depression / mansion**.

2. The good doctor showed a lot of **expansion / compassion**.

3. To go on the field trip, the child needed **permission / omission**.

4. The social worker had a **passion / impression** for her work.

5. The tiger growled as an act of **regression / aggression**.

6. The criminal wrote out his **impression / confession**.

7. The group held a **discussion / emission** on gender issues.

<u>'sion' **after** a vowel</u>

'sion' **after** a vowel has the **/zshun/** sound, and
all vowels are long **except** the 'i' in 'ision':

asion	esion	<u>i</u>sion	osion	usion

*Remember to put new sounds or rules on index cards and have
your student read them every day until they are mastered.*

Read the words below:

abrasion	envision	conclusion
invasion	excision	confusion
occasion	incision	delusion
persuasion	precision	exclusion
adhesion	provision	fusion
cohesion	television	illusion
lesion	vision	intrusion
collision	corrosion	seclusion
decision	erosion	transfusion
division	explosion	

Exercise 40.3
Circle the word that makes the most sense:

1. There was a lot of **<u>decision / confusion</u>** during the earthquake.

2. When you have good eye-sight, you have good **<u>vision / fusion</u>**.

3. The magic show had many **<u>intrusions / illusions</u>**.

4. The cars on the highway were in a **<u>corrosion / collision</u>**.

5. It was an important **<u>provision / decision</u>** that he had to make.

6. Multiplication and **<u>incision / division</u>** are math operations.

Exercise 40.4
Circle the words where 'ea' has the long 'a' sound (there are 5):

hear	swear	break
wear	fear	peak
dear	clear	beak
great	rear	steak

wear
great
swear
break
steak

Exercise 40.5
Circle the **three** words where 'ie' has the long 'i' sound:

shield	tied	field	lied
died	believe	brief	carried

died, tied, lied

Exercise 40.6
Circle the words that are correctly spelled:

1. white / wite
2. hoo / who
3. wut / what
4. climb / clime
5. their / thier
6. anser / answer
7. num / numb
8. when / wen

9. reck / wreck
10. rist / wrist
11. rong / wrong
12. autumn / autum
13. column / colum
14. wuz / was
15. wont / want
16. sed /said

white
who
what
climb
their
answer
numb
when

said
want
was
column
autumn
wrong
wrist
wreck

Exercise 40.7
Do the dictations for this lesson at www.yourkidcanread.com.

Apostrophes for Ownership

When a noun owns something, you add an apostrophe 's'.

I am going to <u>John's</u> house.

If you just added the 's' and not the apostrophe, you would have "Johns", which is the plural form of John, such as:

There are three <u>Johns</u> in my class.

If you have a **plural** noun with ownership, you add the apostrophe **after** the 's':

The <u>dogs'</u> house is large enough for the **three** of them.

Here, there is more than one dog, so we have the word dog in its plural form. The dogs all share a house (ownership), so the apostrophe goes **after** the 's'.

<u>Rules for Apostrophes & Ownership</u>

1. If there is one owner, add an apostrophe and then the 's'.

2. If there is more than one owner, add the 's' and **then** the apostrophe.

3. For nouns ending with an 's', you can either add only the apostrophe, or add an apostrophe 's'. Both ways are acceptable.

Chris' house.

Chris's house.

 The apostrophe in "it's" is **not** for ownership; **it is a contraction for "it is"**

~~It's~~ shape is round.

<u>Its</u> shape is round. ✓

Review; remember, 'al' can sound like /ul/ in many words:

alarm	aloud	lyrical	pedal
alive	alter	medal	petal
allow	always	moral	regal
allowance	animal	optical	rival
almost	equal	optimal	total
aloof	loyal	oval	vital

Review of the 'c' as /s/ words:

accept	cancel	convince	lacy
acceptable	celebrate	convincing	merciful
accelerate	cellar	council	merciless
ace	cemetery	cyclone	mercy
acid	censure	decency	pacific
advance	center	decent	pencil
advice	certain	democracy	policy
agency	certainly	distance	presence
balance	chance	embrace	racing
biceps	cinch	excel	rancid
bicycle	cinder	excitable	recent
brace	circus	excite	recycle
braces	civil	icicle	reference
calcium	concept	icy	rhinoceros

Lesson 41 - Apostrophes for Ownership

Exercise 41.1
Read the following and circle the words that have apostrophes for ownership (if any) **and** draw an arrow to what the noun owns.

1. I believe Emily's neighbor just moved.
2. It's a relief that Tim's house wasn't flooded.
3. Where were you when Sara's dog ran away?
4. Jim's flight may be cancelled due to bad weather.
5. Ethan's girlfriend is coming over later.
6. I like Brandon's new haircut.

1) Emily's (neighbors), 2) Tim's (house), 3) Sara's (dog), 4) Jim's (flight), 5) Ethan's (girlfriend), 6) Brandon's (haircut)

Exercise 41.2
Write the noun on the line using an apostrophe for ownership.

1. The _____ liner is leaking. [pool]

2. My _____ shell is brown. [turtle]

3. The _____ blockparty will be in June. [families*]

4. My _____ cage needs to be cleaned. [birds*]

5. I'm going to _____ house after school. [Tom]

6. My _____ yard needs to be mowed. [neighbor]

7. In the fall, the _____ leaves turn orange. [trees*]

* These are plural words.

pool's, turtle's, families', birds', Tom's, neighbor's, trees'

Review; words with 'tion':

action	direction	motion	reaction
adaption	emotion	operation	section
caption	fraction	option	sensation
correction	function	portion	situation
creation	location	question	solution

Exercise 41.3
Circle the correct ending to the words:

1. celebr_____   ation   etion

2. cond_____   ation   ition

3. sol_____   otion   ution

4. add_____   otion   ition

5. vac_____   ation   ution

6. inform_____   tion   ation

7. combin_____   ution   ation

8. substit_____   ution   otion

(upside-down answer key in left margin:)
celebration
condition
solution
addition
vacation
information
combination
substitution

Exercise 41.4
Answer the questions below:

1. When does 'c' always have the /s/ sound? c____ , c____ , c____

2. When does 'g' sometimes have the /j/ sound? g____ , g____ , g____

3. What letter goes between a **short** vowel and the 'ge'? _____

4. Always use a _____ for the /k/ sound, but use ___ if the /k/ sound
   is followed by an 'e', 'i', or 'y'.

(upside-down answer key:)
1) ce, ci, cy 2) ge, gi, gy 3) d 4) c, k

Exercise 41.5

Circle the sound that makes a real word. Remember, longer words that end with 'ice' end with the /iss/ sound, and longer words ending with 'age' end with the /edge/ sound.

1. just_____ ice age

2. serv_____ ice age

3. man_____ ice age

4. aver_____ ice age

5. not_____ ice age

6. prac_____ ice age

7. pack_____ ice age

8. dam_____ ice age

9. mal_____ ice age

10. mess_____ ice age

justice, service, manage, average, notice, practice, package, damage, malice, message

Exercise 41.6

Add the suffix specified for each word and rewrite the new word:

1. final [ly] _____

2. sneaky [er] _____

3. simple [ly] _____

4. worry [ed] _____

5. heavy [er] _____

6. magnify [ed] _____

7. hurry [ed] _____

8. noisy [er] _____

finally
sneakier
simply
worried
heavier
magnified
hurried
noisier

Exercise 41.7

Do the dictations for this lesson at www.yourkidcanread.com.

Words Ending with Vowels

Many words come from different languages,
and many of those languages are derived from Latin.
Because of this, many times, a vowel will make
a different sound.

Often, the letter 'i' will sound like an 'e'.
We see this in words like:

pizza   piano   pita

Vowels often come at the end of words,
especially if the word originated from another language.

Words that end with 'o' end with a long 'o' sound:

albino	domino	hypo	potato
also	halo	limo	tomato
banjo	hello	mosquito*	veto
buffalo	hobo	piano*	weirdo
casino*	hydro	polo	zero

audio*   cardio*   radio*   studio*

* In these words, the 'i' sounds like a long 'e'.

Words that end with 'a' end with the /uh/ sound:

Africa	camera	pasta	Santa
Alaska	coma	peninsula	scuba
alfalfa	delta	pizza	soda
arena	magma	saliva	sofa
Aruba	panda	salsa	tuna

Words that end with 'ia' end with long 'e' then /uh/:

Amelia	criteria	hysteria	insomnia
bacteria	Cynthia	India	mania
Columbia	dyslexia	inertia	phobia*

 Words that end with 'i' end with the long 'e' sound:

Capri	Fuji	maxi	Pepsi	spaghetti
Chili	Jacuzzi	mini	quasi	taxi
confetti	khaki	Omni	semi	zucchini*

 Words that end with 'u' end with the /oo/ sound:

guru	Zulu	thru	tofu	snafu

* The underlined sounds have not yet been covered.

Read the following:

1. Amelia wore khaki pants when she went to Africa.
2. Maria likes to eat chili with tofu while sitting in her Jacuzzi.
3. Patti will drink Pepsi cola and eat spaghetti.
4. Should we take our mini-van or a taxi?
5. On vacation we might go to Fuji or Columbia.
6. Amelia was up all night with insomnia.
7. Maria has to take a trip to India.
8. I will play the banjo while I also listen to the radio.
9. The president will veto the bill for the new law.
10. We love to eat pizza pita pockets with salsa.

-211-

Read the following:

place - palace	bold - blood	bond - bound
produce - product	fold - flood	pond - pound
quiet - quite	three - tree	from - form
trail - trial	fond - found	charge - change

pause	numb	neighbor	bacteria
autumn	thumb	dyslexia	halo
autistic	field	hysteria	solo
symbolic	brief	bacteria	studio
mystery	relief	studio	radio
waitress	fierce	radio	stereo
distress	pierce	stereo	Columbia
success	believe	Columbia	Argentina
access	belief	Argentina	America
knit	receive	America	Montana
kneel	eight	hysteria	Chili

Exercise 42.1

Write the words for the pictures below:

1. _ _ _ _ _

2. _ _ _ _ _

3. _ _ _ _

4. _ _ _ _ _

5.  _ _ _ _

6.  _ _ _ _ _

7.  _ _ _ _ _ _

8.  _ _ _ _ _ _

zebra, pizza, taxi, radio, tuba, panda, potato, tomato

Exercise 42.2

Circle the sound for the **ending** vowel or vowels in the following words:

1. bacteria   'e'   'i'   'o'   /oo/   /uh/   'e' then /uh/

2. taxi   'e'   'i'   'o'   /oo/   /uh/   'e' then /uh/

3. halo   'e'   'i'   'o'   /oo/   /uh/   'e' then /uh/

4. hero   'e'   'i'   'o'   /oo/   /uh/   'e' then /uh/

5. pizza   'e'   'i'   'o'   /oo/   /uh/   'e' then /uh/

6. quasi   'e'   'i'   'o'   /oo/   /uh/   'e' then /uh/

7. limo   'e'   'i'   'o'   /oo/   /uh/   'e' then /uh/

8. semi   'e'   'i'   'o'   /oo/   /uh/   'e' then /uh/

9. hysteria   'e'   'i'   'o'   /oo/   /uh/   'e' then /uh/

10. sofa   'e'   'i'   'o'   /oo/   /uh/   'e' then /uh/

11. criteria   'e'   'i'   'o'   /oo/   /uh/   'e' then /uh/

12. zero   'e'   'i'   'o'   /oo/   /uh/   'e' then /uh/

13. comma   'e'   'i'   'o'   /oo/   /uh/   'e' then /uh/

14. snafu   'e'   'i'   'o'   /oo/   /uh/   'e' then /uh/

15. guru   'e'   'i'   'o'   /oo/   /uh/   'e' then /uh/

16. potato   'e'   'i'   'o'   /oo/   /uh/   'e' then /uh/

17. arena   'e'   'i'   'o'   /oo/   /uh/   'e' then /uh/

18. pasta   'e'   'i'   'o'   /oo/   /uh/   'e' then /uh/

19. khaki   'e'   'i'   'o'   /oo/   /uh/   'e' then /uh/

19 - e
18 - uh
17 - uh
16 - o
15 - /oo/
14 - /oo/
13 - uh
12 - o
11 - e then /uh/
10 - uh
9 - e then /uh/
8 - e
7 - o
6 - e
5 - uh
4 - o
3 - o
2 - e
1 - e then /uh/

A Workbook for Dyslexics - Cheryl Orlassino   -213-

Exercise 42.3
Fill in the blank with the word that makes the most sense:

buffalo	hysteria	bacteria	confetti	mini
taxi	America	tomato	tornado	scuba

1. We took a _____ from the subway to the Empire States Building.

2. We took the _____ - van to the soccer game.

3. On New Year's Eve, _____ littered the streets.

4. The _____ swept through the small town in Idaho.

5. My vegetable garden had many _____ plants.

6. U.S.A. stands for the United States of _____.

7. Talk of a virus spreading across the globe can result in mass _____.

8. On vacation, we will go _____ diving in the coral reef.

9. The Native Americans hunted _____ on the plains.

10. In science class, we learned about microscopic _____.

A Workbook for Dyslexics - Cheryl Orlassino   -214-

Exercise 42.4

Fill in the blank with the correct word. Words may be used more than once or not at all:

1. She has _____ many pairs of shoes.
   to - too - two

2. We went to _____ house last night.
   there - their - they're

3. They were relieved to find _____ lost dog.
   there - their - they're

4. The singer sang _____ the crowd of people.
   to - too - two

5. I heard _____ going to rain on Saturday.
   its - it's

6. We didn't know _____ Jim went last night.
   where - were - we're

7. The teens like to listen to _____ music.
   there - their - they're

8. _____ are many types of words you should know.
   There - Their - They're

9. What _____ the scientists going to study?
   where - were - we're

10. My little brother wanted to go _____ .
    there - their - they're

11. The taxi made _____ way through the city streets.
    its - it's

12. The confused woman didn't know what _____ do.
    to - too - two

too, their, their, to, it's, where, their, There, were, too, its, to

Exercise 42.5

Do the dictations for this lesson at www.yourkidcanread.com.

-215-

'le', at the end of a word, makes the
/l/ sound, *and* it acts like a vowel.

'le', at the end of a word, makes the /l/ sound,
as in "puzz<u>le</u>". *'le' acts like a vowel.

puzz<u>le</u>   litt<u>le</u>   app<u>le</u>

**Notice how the consonants before the 'le
are <u>doubled</u> to protect the short vowels.**

Read the words below:

ample	bubble	cripple	kettle
angle	cable	cuddle	little
ankle	candle	dangle	middle
apple	cattle	dimple	puzzle
battle	couple	giggle	riddle
bottle	crinkle	handle	settle

The suffix **'ible'** & **'able'** both end with 'le'. The 'i' in 'ible' is *usually* short, and the 'a' in 'able' can be long or short. Read the words below:

accessible	credible	forgivable	sensible
admirable	curable	honorable	stable
audible	detectable	horrible	table
breakable	disable	invisible	terrible
consolable	edible	irresistible	unable
controllable	fable	possible	valuable
convertible	flexible	retractable	visible

Usually 'able' is added to a **complete** word:

break - **break**able   honor - **honor**able

comfort - **comfort**able   cure - **cur**able

Usually 'ible' is **part** of a word:

possible   edible

audible   terrible

 When adding 'able' to a word ending with an 'e',
you can usually take the 'e' out and add 'able'.
However, you can NOT take the 'e' out if you need
it to make a 'g' a /j/ sound, or a 'c' a /s/ sound.

cure - cur**able**   notice - notice**able**

admire - admir**able**   change - change**able**

Exercise 43.1
Read the sentences below, and add '**able**' or '**ible**' to complete the words:

1. The sun was not **vis**__ __ __ __.

2. Anything is **poss**__ __ __ __.

3. Glass is **break**__ __ __ __.

4. The food was not **ed**__ __ __ __.

5. The necklace is **valu**__ __ __ __.

6. The smell was not **detect**__ __ __ __.

7. The story was not **cred**__ __ __ __.

visible, possible, breakable, edible, valuable, detectable, credible

Exercise 43.2
Fill in the letters to make the words for the pictures below (each word ends with 'le'):

1. _ _ _ _ _ _

2. _ _ _ _ _

3. _ _ _ _ _ _

4. _ _ _ _ _ _

5. _ _ _ _ _ _

6. _ _ _ _ _ _

7. _ _ _ _ _ _

8. _ _ _ _ _

kettle, apple, bottle, puzzle,
candle, handle, bubble, ankle

Exercise 43.3
Circle the word that makes the most sense:

1. The sunroof for our patio is **edible / retractable**.

2. The dancer is very **flexible / breakable**.

3. The chocolate cake was **invisible / irresistible**.

4. It's very **terrible / admirable** how you help people.

5. The boy's behavior was **questionable / audible**.

6. The deck was not **possible / assessable** for a wheel chair.

7. The price of the meals are very **detectable / sensible**.

8. The disease was not **visible / curable**.

9. The broken down car was not **drivable / convertible**.

10. The large group of children was not **horrible / manageable**.

Exercise 43.4
Draw lines to match the sounds below (some sounds, on the right, are used more than once):

1.	tion	
2.	oa	
3.	oi	ew
4.	sion	ur
5.	ou	ea
6.	igh	oy
7.	ay	ie
8.	oo	shun
9.	er	shuhl
10.	tial	ai
11.	cial	ow_1
12.	ee	ow_2
13.	ir	

tion-shun, oa-ow, oi-oy, sion-shun, ou-ow, igh-ie,
ay-ai, oo-ew, er-ur, tial-shuhl, cial-shuhl, ee-ea, ir-ur

Exercise 43.5
Circle the words that have the rule breaker short 'e' sound (there are 11):

bread	ready	weather	fountain
lean	heat	teacher	mountain
stream	cheap	reach	certain
instead	bean	stream	trainer
heavy	feather	steady	said

said
certain
mountain
fountain
steady
weather
feather
ready
heavy
instead
bread

Review; read the words below:

perceive	weight	residential	hysteria
deceive	weigh	confidential	bacteria
conceited	treasure	essential	disposable
achieved	measure	credential	cuddle
grief	pleasure	execution	bubble
brief	leather	caution	resistible
field	feather	relationship	terrible
fountain	special	permission	probable
certain	crucial	conversation	dimple
curtain	partial	conversion	dangle
eight	facial	zero	tangle
freight	spatial	solo	tumble

Exercise 43.6

Circle the word that makes the most sense:

1. **There / Their / They're** putting a new roof on the house.

2. **Jim's / Jims** special leather jacket was missing.

3. All the **homes / home's** in my neighborhood are huge.

4. We're going to **there / their** graduation at the end of June.

5. There's **to / too** many ways to answer the question.

6. **Where / Were** did the horrible smell originate from?

7. **There / Their** are two versions of the same story.

8. The ingredients, for the snack, **were / where** mostly artificial.

They're, Jim's, homes, their, too, Where, There, were

Exercise 43.7
Add the suffix specified for each word and rewrite the new word:

> To add 'ly' to a word ending with 'le',
> remove the 'le' and add the 'ly'.

1. sudden [ly]   _____

2. horrible [ly]   _____

3. average [ed]   _____

4. ship [ed]   _____

5. tangle [ed]   _____

6. sprinkle [ing]   _____

7. puzzle [ing]   _____

8. wrinkle [ly]   _____

9. usual [ly]   _____

10. peaceful [ly]   _____

11. notice [able]   _____

12. exchange [able]   _____

13. manage [able]   _____

14. equal [ly]   _____

suddenly, horribly, averaged, shipped, tangled, sprinkling, puzzling, wrinkly, usually, peacefully, noticeable, exchangeable, manageable, equally

Exercise 43.8
Do the dictations for this lesson at www.yourkidcanread.com.

Words Ending with 'ture' and 'sure'

'ture', at the end of a word, makes the /chur/ sound.

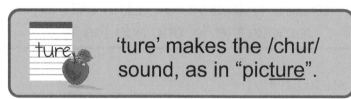

'ture' makes the /chur/ sound, as in "pic**ture**".

picture   future   mixture

Read the following:

adventure	fracture	mature	rupture
capture	furniture	miniature	scripture
caricature	future	mixture	sculpture
culture	gesture	moisture	signature
denture	immature	nature	structure
departure	imposture	pasture	temperature
depicture	juncture	picture	texture
expenditure	lecture	posture	torture
feature	legislature	puncture	venture
fixture	literature	rapture	vulture

Review; read the following:

atch	ance	ow₁	cial	ick	ision
ank	oi	ow₂	ench	onk	usion
ang	ou	inge	ice	ock	ible
ack	er	ation	ace	ar	able
ash	uck	ition	itch	ur	ince
ange	oy	tial	idge	edge	or

'sure' *usually* makes the /shur/ sound.

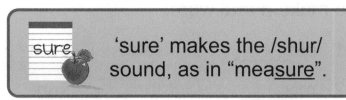

'sure' makes the /shur/ sound, as in "mea<u>sure</u>".

mea<u>sure</u>   pres<u>sure</u>   trea<u>sure</u>

Read the following:

sure	closure	pleasure	leisure
unsure	pressure	treasure	assure
insure	exposure	foreclosure	reassure

Exercise 44.1
Draw lines to match the sounds (sounds on the right may be used more than once):

1. ture

2. tion   long 'a'

3. sure   long 'i'

4. ew   oo

5. igh   oy

6. ay   ow

7. tial   /shun/

8. cial   /chur/

9. sion   /shur/

10. ou   /shuhl/

11. oi

Exercise 44.2
Circle a sound to make a real word:

1.	pic_____	ture	sure
2.	mix____	ture	sure
3.	pres____	ture	sure
4.	mois____	ture	sure
5.	cap____	ture	sure
6.	expo____	ture	sure
7.	fea____	ture	sure
8.	plea____	ture	sure

picture, mixture, pressure, moisture,
capture, exposure, feature, pleasure

Exercise 44.3
Circle a sound to make a real word:

1.	susp_____	ect	ation
2.	inj____	ect	ation
3.	calcul____	ect	ation
4.	re____	act	ition
5.	aud____	act	ition
6.	part____	act	ition
7.	contr____	act	ation
8.	conscentr____	act	ation
9.	n____	act	ation

suspect, inject, calculation, read, audition,
partition, contract, concentration, nation

Exercise 44.4
Read each sentence and circle the word that is correctly spelled:

1. I wasn't sure **wen / when** Emily would be home.

2. There is only **wun / one** thing left to do on our vacation.

3. The situation **wuz / was** not very pleasant.

4. **Hoo / Who** will be coming to our celebration?

5. **Where / Ware** did they capture the criminal?

6. To measure the wood, **yooz / use** the yard stick.

7. She only wanted to see the nature video **wuns / once**.

Exercise 44.5
Write the names of the colors below:

1. ⬤ _ _ _ _ _ _   4. ⬤ _ _ _ _ _

2. ⬤ _ _ _ _ _   5. ⬤ _ _ _ _ _ _

3. ⬤ _ _ _ _ _ _   6. ⬤ _ _ _ _ _

purple, pink, orange, green, yellow, blue

Exercise 44.6
Circle the sound for the letters that are underlined:

1. w<u>i</u>ld	long 'e'	long 'i'	5. cont<u>ro</u>l	long 'o'	short 'o'
2. m<u>o</u>st	long 'o'	short 'o'	6. f<u>o</u>lder	long 'o'	short 'o'
3. m<u>igh</u>t	long 'i'	short 'i'	7. ch<u>i</u>ld	long 'i'	short 'i'
4. wh<u>a</u>t	short 'a'	short 'u'	8. ch<u>i</u>ldren	long 'i'	short 'i'

long i, long o, long i, short u, long o, long i, long o, short i

Exercise 45.7
Complete the words for the pictures below:

1.   mea__ __ __ __

3.   trea __ __ __ __

2.   pic __ __ __ __

4.   vul__ __ __ __

measure, picture, treasure, vulture

Exercise 45.8
Below is a review for rule breakers. Fill in the blanks:

1. 'ea' can be a **long** '____', as in: b __ __ __ __

2. 'ea' can be a **short** '____', as in: b __ __ __ __

3. 'ea' can be a **long** '____', as in: p __ __ __
   (in 8 words only)

4. 'ai' can be a **long** '____', as in: p __ __ __

5. 'ai' can be a **short** '____', as in: foun __ __ __ __

6. 'ie' can be a **long** '____', as in: __ __ __

7. 'ie' can be a **long** '____', as in: sh__ __ __ __

8. 'ei' can be a **long** '____', as in: __ __ ght   8

e-beach, e-bread, a-pear, a-pail,
e-fountain, e-pie, e-shield, a-eight

Exercise 44.9
Identify and circle what the 'y', in the following words, sounds like:

1.	abyss	long 'i'	short 'i'
2.	cynical	long 'i'	short 'i'
3.	crypt	long 'i'	short 'i'
4.	cycle	long 'i'	short 'i'
5.	pyramid	long 'i'	short 'i'
6.	cyber	long 'i'	short 'i'
7.	cylinder	long 'i'	short 'i'
8.	systematic	long 'i'	short 'i'

1) short i
2) short i
3) short i
4) long i
5) short i
6) long i
7) short i
8) short i

Exercise 44.10
Make the following words past tense:

1. notify _____

2. supply _____

3. rectify _____

4. decide _____

5. carry _____

6. ship _____

7. worry _____

8. hurry _____

9. race _____

10. stand _____

11. draw _____

12. plan _____

notified, supplied, rectified, decided, carried, shipped, worried, hurried, raced, stood, drew, planned

Exercise 44.11
Do the dictations for this lesson at www.yourkidcanread.com.

-227-

'ous' makes the /us/ sound.

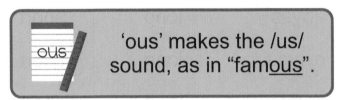

'ous' makes the /us/ sound, as in "fam**ous**".

fam**ous**   danger**ous**   glamor**ous**

Read the following:

adventurous	erroneous	jealous	numerous
ambitious	famous	luminous	previous
callous	generous	marvelous	religious
continuous	glamorous	monotonous	ridiculous
dangerous	gorgeous	nauseous	simultaneous
disastrous	humorous	nervous	zealous

'ious' *usually* makes the 'e'- /us/ sound.

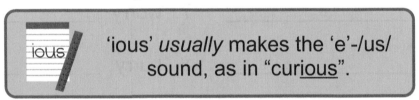

'ious' *usually* makes the 'e'-/us/ sound, as in "cur**ious**".

cur**ious**   ser**ious**   hilar**ious**

Read the following:

copious	furious	luxurious	serious
curious	glorious	mysterious	studious
devious	hilarious	oblivious	tedious
dubious	illustrious	obvious	various
envious	insidious	previous	vicarious

cious   tious   xious

If 'ious' *follows* a 'c', 't' or 'x', then those letters combined with 'ious' sounds like /shus/.

Read the following; remember, '**ci**ous' = /shus/:

atrocious	malicious	suspicious
delicious	precious	tenacious
gracious	semiconscious	unconscious
judicious	spacious	vivacious

Read the following; remember, '**ti**ous' = /shus/:

ambitious	infectious	repetitious
cautious	nutritious	scrumptious
expeditious	ostentatious	superstitious
fictitious	pretentious	
flirtatious	rambunctious	

Read the following; remember, '**xi**ous' = /shus/:

anxious   noxious   obnoxious

Exercise 45.1
Circle the sounds to make a real word:

1. nerv____   ious   ous   6. var____   ious   ous

2. cur____   ious   ous   7. ser____   ious   ous

3. numer____   ious   ous   8. obliv____   ious   ous

4. danger____   ious   ous   9. glamor____   ious   ous

5. fur____   ious   ous   10. marvel____   ious   ous

nervous, curious, numerous, dangerous, furious,
various, serious, oblivious, glamorous, marvelous

Exercise 45.2
For each sentence, choose the word that makes sense:

vulture	fractured	tedious	temperature
obvious	texture	immature	ventured
pasture	future	puncture	picture

1. The sheep were out in the _____.

2. The _____ of the satin cloth was silky soft.

3. A gypsy looks into a crystal ball to see your _____.

4. A _____ of his girlfriend was on the table.

5. The boy fell and _____ his arm.

6. I will _____ the balloon with a needle.

7. The _____ outside is ninety degrees.

8. The _____ circled overhead.

9. The mouse _____ out of the hole in the wall.

10. Another word for boring is _____.

11. Her little sister can act so _____.

12. The answer to the problem was _____.

Exercise 45.3
Circle a sound to make a real word:

1. cap____   ture   ition
2. pic____   ture   ition
3. pet____   ture   ition
4. rend____   ture   ition
5. fu____   ture   ition

6. ver____   sure   sion
7. pres____   sure   sion
8. mea____   sure   sion
9. ses____   sure   sion
10. in____   sure   sion

capture, picture, petition, rendition, future,
version, pressure, measure, session, insure

Exercise 45.4
Circle the word that makes the most sense:

1. An egg is very **famous / nutritious**.

2. Walking alone in a dark alley is very **humorous / dangerous**.

3. The strawberry dessert was **delicious / generous**.

4. The **furious / glamorous** movie star walked down the red carpet.

5. The **continuous / curious** boy raised his hand to ask a question.

6. You must be extra **obvious / cautious** when walking on ice.

7. When you are sea-sick you get very **jealous / nauseous**.

8. When something is funny it is **hilarious / serious**.

9. The high priced hotel resort was **ridiculous / luxurious**.

Read the following sounds:

etch	idge	ous	ew	ict
itch	ange	ious	ind	ar
ack	inge	ou	igh	or
ank	unge	oy	anch	ur
ing	tion	oo	unch	ir
ung	sion	oi	ay	alk
ice	tial	ow_1	ace	ence
ance	cial	ow_2	au	ick

Exercise 45.5

Draw lines to match the words on the left to the rhyming words on the right:

1.	come	tiled
2.	mild	dancer
3.	could	hold
4.	stern	numb
5.	field	act
6.	scrolled	style
7.	fight	kneeled
8.	answer	kite
9.	backed	run
10.	while	burn
11.	done	hood

come-numb, mild-tiled, could-hood, stern-burn, field-kneeled,
scrolled-hold, fight-kite, answer-dancer, backed-act, while-style, done-run

Exercise 45.6

Draw lines to match the definitions on the left to their words on the right:

1. Having the same value: version

2. A different form of something: population

3. To change something: equal

4. Acting more than your age: insomnia

5. Likes to be around others: imitation

6. Not the real thing: zero

7. An amount of people living in a place: alter

8. When two things hit each other: social

9. A number meaning "nothing":   mature

10. Trouble sleeping: collision

Exercise 45.7

Circle the "they're", "there', and "their" words which are not correctly used:

1. **They're** car was in a collision.

2. The motion of the boat made **their** child nauseous.

3. **There** is an obvious answer to the question.

4. The college students were serious about **there** classes.

5. **Their** are numerous reasons why people shouldn't smoke.

1. Their, 2. correct, 3. correct, 4. their, 5. There

Exercise 45.8

Do the dictations for this lesson at www.yourkidcanread.com.

Words Ending with the /v/ Sound

There are two facts about the letter 'v':

1. Letter 'v' is never **doubled** to protect a short vowel (except for the words: "divvy", "savvy" & "skivvy"). We saw this in an earlier lesson:

 The following consonants are **never** doubled:

c h j k q v̲ w x y

2. A word will **never end with the letter 'v'**. It will always have a 've', and the 'e' may or may not be used to turn a vowel long.

 A word that ends with /v/ ends with 've'.

Read the following; in the words below, the last 'e' does NOT turn a vowel long.

abusive	conductive	give	permissive
active	creative	inventive	positive
adhesive	cursive	live	relative
adjective	deserve	massive	repetitive
aggressive	elective	motive	restrictive
appreciative	expensive	negative	sedative
assertive	explosive	obsessive	sensitive
captive	expressive	offensive	submissive
collective	evolve	olive	talkative
compulsive	festive	passive	twelve

lo̲ve̲ = /luv/   glo̲ve̲ = /gluv/   abo̲ve̲ = /ubbuv/

* Note that the three words above, share the same sound.

Read the following; in the words below, the last 'e' **does** turn a vowel long.

alive	contrive	drive	live
arrive	deprive	five	revive
chive	derive	hive	strive
connive	dive	jive	survive

Sometimes you have to read the sentence to know which way to read a word:

Someday, I'd like to <u>live</u> near a <u>live</u> horse farm.

I <u>read</u> a book, on how to <u>read</u> facial expressions.

Read the following words which end with the /v/ sound (remember the 'c' as /s/ rule and 'ie' is a double vowel rule breaker):

conceive	deceive	perceive	receive
achieve	believe	grieve	retrieve

 For words that end with /j/ use: **ge**
 For words that end with /v/ use: **ve**

Read the following:

1. The lady never learned to drive.
2. He never wore the leather gloves that I gave him.
3. My relatives are very active in their community.
4. I'm taking a creative writing class.
5. The heavy man was put on a restrictive diet.
6. The woman's skin is sensitive to sunlight.
7. The opposite of positive is negative.

Exercise 46.1
Choose the word that makes sense and write it on the line:

revive	talkative	survive	motive
protective	massive	active	festive

1. The colorful party lights were very _____.

2. The castaways had to get along in order to _____.

3. The energetic kitten was very _____.

4. The paramedics tried to _____ the man.

5. The detective tried to find a _____ for the crime.

6. The teenage girls were very _____.

7. When something is very large, it is _____.

8. The mother bear was very _____ of her babies.

Exercise 46.2
Circle a sound to make a real word:

1. talkat____   ive   ision   ous

2. div____   ive   ision   ous

3. danger____   ive   ision   ous

4. v____   ive   ision   ous

5. elect____   ive   ision   ous

talkative, division, dangerous, vision, elective

Read the following:

adventure	miniature	pasture	temperature
fixture	mixture	picture	texture
fracture	moisture	signature	torture
mature	nature	structure	venture
captivation	education	position	relation
commotion	invasion	potion	solution
confusion	limitation	question	station
decision	lotion	quotation	summation
division	motion	reduction	vision

Exercise 46.3

Add the ending listed to the word:

1. repulsive [ly] _____

2. torture [ed] _____

3. survive [ing] _____

4. creative [ly] _____

5. sleepy [ly] _____

6. tentative [ly] _____

7. venture [ed] _____

repulsively, tortured, surviving, creatively,
sleepily, tentatively, ventured

Exercise 46.4

Do the dictations for this lesson at www.yourkidcanread.com.

'ch' as /sh/ and /k/

Since our language evolved over time and was influenced by other languages, we often have different sounds for certain letter groups. In this lesson, we will see that 'ch' not only has the /ch/ sound as in "chop", but it has two other sounds: /sh/ and /k/.

'ch' as /sh/ comes from the French,
and 'ch' as /k/ comes from the Greeks.

 When a word is "French" in nature, 'ch' = /sh/:

brochure	chateau	chivalry	chaise
cache	chauffeur	chute	mustache
cachet	chauvinist	cliché	niche
chagrin	chef	crochet	parachute
chalet	chemise	douche	pistachio
champagne	chic	fuchsia	quiche
chandelier	Chicago	louche	ricochet
chaperone	chiffon	machete	ruche
charade	chinook	machine	
charlatan	chivalrous	Michigan	

Note that in French derived words:

ou = /oo/:   s<u>ou</u>p   gr<u>ou</u>p   d<u>ou</u>che   l<u>ou</u>che

Words ending with 'et', end with long 'a' sound:

ricoch<u>et</u> = /rik oa shay/   chal<u>et</u> = /sh al ay/

'e' often sounds like long 'a': cach<u>e</u>

'i' often sounds like long 'e': mach<u>i</u>ne   cl<u>i</u>che   ch<u>i</u>c

<u>When a word is technical, musical or medical, 'ch' = /k/:</u>
* These words usually come from the Greek language.

ache	chlorophyll	ochlocracy
anchor	chord	oligarchy
Anchorage	chorus	orchid
archaic	Christmas	schedule
archangel	chrome	scheme
archeology	chronic	Schenectady
architect	chrysanthemum	schism
chameleon	conch	schizophrenic
chaos	echo	scholar
character	epoch	scholastic
characteristic	ichthyology	school
charisma	inchoate	schooner
chasm	mechanic	stomach
chemist	mitochondria	synchronize
chemistry	monarch	
chlorine	monarchy	

Exercise 47.1
Circle the words where 'ch' has the /k/ sound (there are 6):

charismatic	chief	chord	chemistry
charter	chlorine	charity	chunkier
chapter	chagrin	cherish	character
chef	chaos	church	chance

charismatic, chlorine, chaos, chord, chemistry, character

Exercise 47.2
Circle the word that goes with the given definition:

1. Needlework done by a needle with a hook at one end:

   crockery   brochure   crochet

2. Hair that grows under the nose, above the upper lip:

   mustard   mustache   machine

3. A person who drives a car for another person:

   chaperone   chauffeur   chauvinist

4. A type of nut:

   pistachio   fuchsia   chemise

5. A fancy lighting device that hangs from the ceiling:

   chateau   cachet   chandelier

6. A large city in Illinois:

   Michigan   Chicago   Champlain

7. A device that is made to perform a function:

   machine   marine   magazine

8. The person who accompanies a group in order to supervise:

   charlatan   chauffeur   chaperone

9. A tube that something can pass through:

   chute   niche   parachute

10. A deception, pretending to be someone else:

    charade   chaperone   chauffeur

11. A common expression, often overused:

    cleaver   brochure   cliché

Exercise 47.3
Circle the sounds that match the underlined letter(s):

1. e<u>ch</u>o	/shun/	/shuhl/	/k/	/sh/	/ou/	long 'a'	long 'o'
2. <u>ch</u>ef	/shun/	/shuhl/	/k/	/sh/	/ou/	long 'a'	long 'o'
3. s<u>ch</u>ool	/shun/	/shuhl/	/k/	/sh/	/ou/	long 'a'	long 'o'
4. cond<u>iti</u>on	/shun/	/shuhl/	/k/	/sh/	/ou/	long 'a'	long 'o'
5. or<u>ch</u>id	/shun/	/shuhl/	/k/	/sh/	/ou/	long 'a'	long 'o'
6. br<u>ea</u>k	/shun/	/shuhl/	/k/	/sh/	/ou/	long 'a'	long 'o'
7. foll<u>ow</u>	/shun/	/shuhl/	/k/	/sh/	/ou/	long 'a'	long 'o'
8. in<u>iti</u>ally	/shun/	/shuhl/	/k/	/sh/	/ou/	long 'a'	long 'o'
9. s<u>ch</u>eme	/shun/	/shuhl/	/k/	/sh/	/ou/	long 'a'	long 'o'
10. all<u>ow</u>	/shun/	/shuhl/	/k/	/sh/	/ou/	long 'a'	long 'o'
11. mis<u>sion</u>	/shun/	/shuhl/	/k/	/sh/	/ou/	long 'a'	long 'o'
12. attrac<u>tion</u>	/shun/	/shuhl/	/k/	/sh/	/ou/	long 'a'	long 'o'
13. spe<u>cial</u>	/shun/	/shuhl/	/k/	/sh/	/ou/	long 'a'	long 'o'
14. gr<u>ea</u>tly	/shun/	/shuhl/	/k/	/sh/	/ou/	long 'a'	long 'o'
15. essen<u>tial</u>	/shun/	/shuhl/	/k/	/sh/	/ou/	long 'a'	long 'o'

1) /k/, 2) /sh/, 3) /k/, 4) /shun/, 5) /k/, 6) long 'o', 7) long 'a', 8) /shuhl/ 9) /k/, 10) /ou/, 11) /shun/, 12) /shun/, 13) /shuhl/, 14) long 'a', 15) /shuhl/

Exercise 47.4
Circle the double vowel rule breakers (there are 7):

pear	wear	dear	great
steak	bear	weak	fear
rear	swear	leak	beak
gear	near	bead	break

pear, steak, wear, bear, swear, great, break

Read the following sounds:

tial	atch	unk	ation	ang
ition	ous	sure	alk	ung
ew	udge	ance	ice	ick
inge	ious	ou	ank	ink
ision	ture	itch	ong	uck
au	th	oi	ace	oy
ince	oo	igh	aw	ange

Exercise 47.5
Circle the words that are correctly spelled:

1.	thum	thumb	11.	rhyme	ryme
2.	climb	clime	12.	herb	erb
3.	answer	anser	13.	bom	bomb
4.	toard	toward	14.	dumb	dum
5.	plummer	plumber	15.	nife	knife
6.	sword	sord	16.	knock	nock
7.	iland	island	17.	wrist	rist
8.	honor	onnor	18.	neel	kneel
9.	det	debt	19.	colum	column
10.	gnarl	narl	20.	wrinkle	rinkle

Exercise 47.6
Do the dictations for this lesson at www.yourkidcanread.com.

'ph' *always* makes the /f/ sound.

'ph' makes the /f/ sound as in "<u>ph</u>ony".

<u>ph</u>ony   dol<u>ph</u>in   mor<u>ph</u>

Read the following:

alpha	emphasize	phase	phrase
amphibian	graph	phobia	prophesy
asphalt	graphic	phobic	prophets
autograph	morph	phone	sapphire
cellophane	orphan	phonics	sophisticated
chlorophyll	orphanage	phony	sphere
dolphin	pamphlet	photo	symphony
elephant	phantom	photogenic	triumph
emphasis	pharmacist	photon	trophy

'gh' is often silent, but *sometimes*, like 'ph', it has the /f/ sound. Note that in many of these words, there are vowels that do nothing.

laugh = /laff/   rough = /ruff/

trough = /trawf/   tough = /tuff/

cough = /cawf/   enough = /enuf/

'gh' as /f/ is not very popular, and most of the words are listed above.

Exercise 48.1
Circle the word that corresponds to the given meaning:

1. When something is funny, people tend to:

   morph   cough   laugh

2. When you win first place in a contest, you may recieve a:

   trophy   triumph   sphere

3. A semi-precious stone, that is blue in color:

   sphere   photon   sapphire

4. A gray animal that swims in the sea:

   elephant   dolphin   phantom

5. Having an abnormal fear of something:

   phobic   phobia   enough

6. A child who does not have parents:

   orphanage   orphan   tough

7. This is found in the leaves of plants:

   chlorophyll   photons   asphalt

8. The opposite of smooth:

   tough   rough   cough

9. The shape of a ball, or a globe, is a:

   sapphire   graph   sphere

10. An elaborate musical composition:

    photo   sophisticated   symphony

Read the following:

furniture	socially	captivated	invitation
venture	tentative	motive	vacation
adventure	sensitive	attractive	location
separately	actively	massive	reaction
nervously	survive	decision	dangerous
capture	survival	vision	cautious
partially	captive	visionary	delicious

Exercise 48.2

In each sentence, circle the word that makes the most sense:

1. The **cautious / artificial** sweetener tasted bitter.

2. The math class had an **emphasize / emphasis** on algebra.

3. The chemistry teacher wanted us to **morph / graph** our data.

4. There are many **phases / sessions** of the moon.

5. You may win a trophy if you are **triumphant / trumpet**.

6. A(n) **dolphin / elephant** is a large mammal with a trunk.

7. The **phobic / phony** diamond was nothing but glass.

8. We followed the **official / graphic** rules when we played.

9. I went to the doctor's office because I had a **photo / cough**.

10. Oranges and apples are very **sophisticated / nutritious**.

'aught' & 'ought' both have the /awt/ sound.

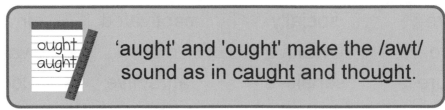

'aught' and 'ought' make the /awt/ sound as in <u>caught</u> and th<u>ought</u>.

<u>caught</u>   th<u>ought</u>

Not many words have these sounds, and most are listed below.

Read the following 'aught' words:

caught	fraught	slaughter	naughty
taught	daughter	haughty	onslaught

Read the following 'ought' words:

ought	brought	sought	thoughtful
bought	fought	thought	wrought

An exception: drought = /drout/

'aught' makes sense, since 'au' is /aw/,
and the 'gh' is silent.

<u>au</u>ght = /awt/

However, **'ought'** does not make sense,
since 'ou' makes the /ou/ sound as in "ouch".

When you see 'ou' with the 'ght', it helps to
pretend that the 'o' is an 'a' so you get the /aw/ sound.

Jim <u>caught</u> a fish.

A Workbook for Dyslexics - Cheryl Orlassino   -246-

Exercise 48.3
Write the past tense form of the word on the line:

1. teach   _____

2. fight   _____

3. catch   _____

4. bring   _____

5. think   _____

6. seek   _____

7. buy   _____

8. ship   _____

9. plan   _____

10. happen   _____

11. listen   _____

12. turn   _____

13. learn   _____

14. receive   _____

15. believe   _____

taught, fought, caught, brought, thought, sought, bought, shipped, planned, happened, listened, turned, learned, received, believed

Exercise 48.4
Draw a line to match the sounds:

1. ph   /chur/

2. igh   /shuhl/

3. aught   /shur/

4. sure   long 'i'

5. ous   /shun/

6. ture   /us/

7. sion   /awt/

8. tial   /f/

Exercise 48.5
Fill in the letter that completes the word:

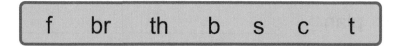

f   br   th   b   s   c   t

1. Neal ____**ough**t Emma was going to be late.

2. We ____**ought** pasta salad to the picnic.

3. The older boy ____**aught** his little brother how to swim.

4. I ____**aught** a cold and ended up with a bad cough.

5. The two countries ____**ought** in a war over land.

6. The lady went to the store and ____**ought** a new outfit.

7. The promising football star was ____**ought** by other teams.

thought, brought, taught, caught, fought, bought, sought

Exercise 48.6
Circle the sounds that match the underlined letter(s):

1. offi<u>ci</u>al	/shun/	/shuhl/	/iss/	/edge/	/shur/
2. mea<u>sure</u>	/shun/	/shuhl/	/iss/	/edge/	/shur/
3. colli<u>si</u>on	/shun/	/shuhl/	/iss/	/edge/	/shur/
4. not<u>ice</u>	/shun/	/shuhl/	/iss/	/edge/	/shur/
5. expo<u>sure</u>	/shun/	/shuhl/	/iss/	/edge/	/shur/
6. pres<u>sure</u>	/shun/	/shuhl/	/iss/	/edge/	/shur/
7. par<u>ti</u>ally	/shun/	/shuhl/	/iss/	/edge/	/shur/
8. serv<u>ice</u>	/shun/	/shuhl/	/iss/	/edge/	/shur/
9. man<u>age</u>	/shun/	/shuhl/	/iss/	/edge/	/shur/
10. ses<u>sion</u>	/shun/	/shuhl/	/iss/	/edge/	/shur/
11. rela<u>tion</u>	/shun/	/shuhl/	/iss/	/edge/	/shur/
12. artifi<u>ci</u>al	/shun/	/shuhl/	/iss/	/edge/	/shur/
13. prac<u>tice</u>	/shun/	/shuhl/	/iss/	/edge/	/shur/
14. commo<u>tion</u>	/shun/	/shuhl/	/iss/	/edge/	/shur/
15. block<u>age</u>	/shun/	/shuhl/	/iss/	/edge/	/shur/
16. ini<u>tial</u>	/shun/	/shuhl/	/iss/	/edge/	/shur/
17. pack<u>age</u>	/shun/	/shuhl/	/iss/	/edge/	/shur/
18. solu<u>tion</u>	/shun/	/shuhl/	/iss/	/edge/	/shur/

1-/shuhl/, 2-/shur/, 3-/shun/, 4-/iss/, 5-/shur/, 6-/shur/, 7-/shuhl/, 8-/iss/, 9-/edge/, 10-/shun/, 11-/shun/, 12-/shuhl/, 13-/iss/, 14-/shun/, 15-/edge/, 16-/shuhl/, 17-/edge/, 18-/shun/

Exercise 48.7
Do the dictations for this lesson at www.yourkidcanread.com.

'ician' makes the /ishun/ sound, where the 'i' is short. Usually words ending with this sound have to do with an occupation.

The first 'i' in 'ician' has the short 'i' sound.

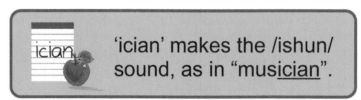

'ician' makes the /ishun/ sound, as in "mus<u>ician</u>".

mus<u>ician</u>   mag<u>ician</u>   techn<u>ician</u>

Read the following:

beauty - beautician	optic - optician
clinic - clinician	pediatric - pediatrician
electric - electrician	physical - physician
music - musician	politics - politician
magic - magician	statistic - statistician
mathematic - mathematician	technical - technician

The three ways to get the /shun/ sound are:

cian   sion   tion

Read the following:

1. The politician ran for public office in November.
2. The electrician fixed the light switch.
3. The magician pulled a rabbit out of his hat.
4. The musician played a song on his guitar.
5. Every year, Nick goes to the pediatrician's for a check-up.

Exercise 49.1
Circle a sound to make a real word. Remember, if the word has to do with an occupation, then it *usually* ends with 'ician'.

		ition	ician	icial
1.	diet____	ition	ician	icial
2.	off____	ition	ician	icial
3.	cond____	ition	ician	icial
4.	part____	ition	ician	icial
5.	electr____	ition	ician	icial
6.	benef____	ition	ician	icial
7.	artif____	ition	ician	icial
8.	phys____	ition	ician	icial
9.	polit____	ition	ician	icial
10.	ed____	ition	ician	icial

dietician, official, condition, partition, electrician, beneficial, artificial, physician, politician, edition

Read the following:

accrue	barbeque	issued	statue
argue	fondue	pursue	tissue
arguing	hue	residue	value
avenue	issue	revenue	virtue
brought	daughter	luscious	phobia
caught	echo	magnify	service
chemical	enough	mechanic	taught
chemist	icicle	notice	thought
chord	intention	noticeable	through
coughing	laughter	ominous	transition

Exercise 49.2
Circle the word on the right, that rhymes with the word on the left:

1.	know	glow	plow	tow
2.	eight	height	heir	late
3.	field	healed	held	pie
4.	what	spat	chat	shut
5.	should	cold	shoulder	stood
7.	mind	win	pinned	shined
8.	height	weigh	fight	weight
9.	climb	dime	limb	thumb
9.	great	greet	eat	wait
10.	pear	fear	hear	fair

glow, late, healed, shut, stood, shined, fight, dime, wait, fair

Exercise 49.3
Circle the sound that the underlined letters make:

1. phase   /f/   /p/

2. echo   /k/   /sh/

3. politician   /ishun/   /shahl/

4. fracture   /tor/   /chur/

5. cautious   /shus/   /us/

6. musician   /ishun/   /shahl/

7. substantial   /tale/   /shahl/

8. measure   /shur/   /shahl/

/shun/
/shahl/
/ishun/
/shus/
/chur/
/ishun/
/k/
/f/

Exercise 49.4
Circle the sounds for the underlined letters:

1. captive — long 'i' — short 'i'
2. wild — long 'i' — short 'i'
3. drive — long 'i' — short 'i'
4. symbol — long 'i' — short 'i'
5. give — long 'i' — short 'i'
6. positive — long 'i' — short 'i'
7. find — long 'i' — short 'i'
8. notify — long 'i' — short 'i'
9. arrive — long 'i' — short 'i'
10. elective — long 'i' — short 'i
11. strive — long 'i' — short 'i'
12. expensive — long 'i' — short 'i'
13. mild — long 'i' — short 'i'
14. child — long 'i' — short 'i'
15. sigh — long 'i' — short 'i'
16. system — long 'i' — short 'i'
17. satisfy — long 'i' — short 'i'
18. bright — long 'i' — short 'i'
19. attractive — long 'i' — short 'i'
20. gigantic — long 'i' — short 'i''

Exercise 49.5

Complete the sentences below with words from the list:

volcano	Africa	phobia
peninsula	dyslexia	tuna
hysteria	vacation	panda

1. The boy ate a _____ fish sandwich.

2. Florida is a _____ state; it has water on three sides.

3. The girl had a _____ ; she was scared of heights.

4. There was much _____ over the arrival of the popular boy band.

5. Both Patti and Cynthia have trouble reading, they may have _____ .

6. On our _____ in Italy, we went to the Island of Capri.

7. The Zulu tribe is located in _____ .

8. The magma exploded from inside the _____ .

9. The _____ bear comes from China.

Exercise 49.6
Complete the sentences below with words from the list:

tradition	pollution	decision
donation	session	solution
addition	imitation	ignition
admiration	motion	condition

1. The smoke stacks gave off a lot of _____.

2. It is a _____ to celebrate birthdays.

3. What is the _____ to the problem?

4. Court is now in _____.

5. For math, children learn _____.

6. My family made a _____ to the charity.

7. The painting was not real; it was an _____.

8. The _____ of the boat, made the boy sick.

9. We had to make a final _____ .

10. I have a lot of _____ for the rescue workers.

11. To start a car, put the key in the _____.

12. The old car was still in good _____.

Exercise 49.7
Do the dictations for this lesson at www.yourkidcanread.com.

Many of our words in the English Language come from the French language. English, as we know it today, wasn't around until the year 1500AD (only 500 years ago). Before that, the people of England spoke different dialects, and were influenced by the people who invaded their land. The French invaded England around 1066AD, bringing with them their language. For a while, the English were only allowed to speak French, which didn't last for long. They soon began speaking English again, but with a French twist. Many of the French words stayed, and today, 30% to 40% of our words are of French origin.

In earlier lessons we saw how we get a /s/ sound when 'c' is followed by an 'e', 'i' or 'y'. We also saw how the 'ch' can have the /sh/ sound (this is for a small amount of words that are French derived). Now we will look at some more French derived words.

Words that end with 'et' end with a long 'a' sound:

ballet	cachet	duvet	sorbet
beret	chalet	filet	valet
bouquet	Chevrolet	gourmet	
buffet	crochet	ricochet	
cabaret	croqet	sachet	

* Remember, 'ch' for French derived words, makes the /sh/ sound.

The French usually pronounce 'ou' as /oo/:

group = /groop/   croup = /croop/

soup = /soop/   wound = /woond/

* We saw these words already.

The French do not pronouce the 'h' at the start of a word:

heir = /air/   honor = /onnor/

honest = /onnest/   hour = /our/

* We saw these words already (silent letters).

The French usually pronounce 'ch' as /sh/:

brochure	chateau	chivalry	chaise
cache	chauffeur	chute	mustache
cachet	chauvinist	cliché	niche
chagrin	chef	crochet	parachute
chalet	chemise	douche	pistachio
champagne	chic	fuchsia	quiche
chandelier	Chicago	louche	ricochet
chaperone	chiffon	machete	ruche
charade	chinook	machine	
charlatan	chivalrous	Michigan	

* We saw these words already.

When adding a suffix to words ending with 'et' as a long 'a', we don't need to double the 't' to protect the short 'e' , since 'e' in 'et' is not short.

ricoch<u>et</u> - ricoch<u>et</u>ed - ricoch<u>et</u>ing - ricoch<u>et</u>s

The bullet will **ricochet** off the brick wall.
The bullet **ricocheted** off the brick wall.
The bullet is **ricocheting** off the wall.
The bullet **ricochets** off the wall.

croch<u>et</u> - croch<u>et</u>ed - croch<u>et</u>ing - croch<u>et</u>s

The woman will **crochet** a blanket.
The woman **crocheted** a blanket.
The woman is **crocheting** a blanket.
The woman **crochets** a blanket.

Read the following:

1. The ballet dancer received a bouquet of flowers.
2. The gourmet chef made a fish filet.
3. For dessert, we had orange sorbet.
4. The valet took the keys to the car.
5. The bullet ricocheted off the tin can.
6. A duvet is a soft quilt used for a bed.
7. The woman crocheted a baby blanket .

Exercise 50.1
Circle the words where 'et' has the long 'a' sound (there are 6):

fill<u>et</u>	bask<u>et</u>	ratch<u>et</u>	bouqu<u>et</u>
qui<u>et</u>	cors<u>et</u>	gourm<u>et</u>	buff<u>et</u>
ball<u>et</u>	croch<u>et</u>	val<u>et</u>	ankl<u>et</u>

fillet, ballet, crochet, gourmet, valet, bouquet

Review:

elective	festivity	assert	captivate
elector	permissive	assertion	captivating
electee	permission	asserting	obsess
election	repeat	assertive	obsessing
festive	repeating	captive	obsessive
festival	repetitive	caption	obsession

Exercise 50.2
Circle the correct word for the sentence:

1. At the breakfast buffet, I had (sum , some) bacon and eggs.

2. It took the turtle an hour to cross the (road , rode).

3. We took an air- (plane , plain) to Paris.

4. For (desert , dessert) I had the orange sorbet.

5. I lost weight and my jeans were (too , to) (loose , lose).

6. Try not to (loose , lose) your car keys.

7. The chef (maid , made) a fillet of fish for dinner.

8. The French artist (wares , wears) a beret on his head.

9. Sandpaper is (course , coarse) and bumpy.

10. We laid out the croquet (course , coarse) in the backyard.

11. The eagle will (sore , soar) (threw , through) the sky.

12. The ballet dancer wore a tutu around her (waist , waste).

13. The wind (blew , blue) dirt onto the (would , wood) floor.

wears, coarse, course, soar, through, waist, blew, wood
some, road, plane, dessert, too, loose, lose, made,

Review:

might	caught	laughter	victorious
right	taught	rough	curious
bright	daughter	tough	revision
slight	eight	enough	intrusion
tight	weight	initial	session
fought	freight	signature	invention
brought	cough	cautious	condition
thought	laugh	precious	station

Exercise 50.3
Write the un-contracted words on the lines:

1. couldn't _____

2. didn't _____

3. that's _____

4. they've _____

5. weren't _____

6. you've _____

7. we've _____

8. it'll _____

9. doesn't _____

10. she's _____

11. I'm _____

12. I'll _____

13. he'll _____

14. don't _____

15. we'll _____

16. I've _____

could not, did not, that is, they have, were not, you have, we have, it will does not, she is, I am, I will, he will, do not, we will, I have

Exercise 50.4
Do the dictations for this lesson at www.yourkidcanread.com.

A Workbook for Dyslexics - Cheryl Orlassino -260-

In earlier lessons, we saw how to add the following suffixes: 'ing', 'ed' (for past tense words), 'ly', and 'er'. In this lesson, we will add the suffix 'est', which follows the same rules as 'er'.

Just like 'er', we add 'est' to **adjectives** (words that *describe* nouns), such as "loudest", "softest", or "nearest". The suffixes 'er' and 'est' are related, see the sentence below:

Bill is loud, Sarah is loud**er**, but Sam is the loud**est**.

We add the suffix 'est' when comparing more than two nouns.

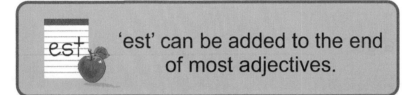

'est' can be added to the end of most adjectives.

happi**est**   sadd**est**   quick**est**

Rules for Adding 'est'

1. If the word ends with a consonant followed by a y, change the 'y' to an 'i', then add the 'est'.
Note that the 'i' will sound like a long 'e' in these words.

hap**py** - happ**iest**

2. If the word ends with an 'e': Just add the 'st':

fin**e** - fin**est**

3. Since 'est' starts with a vowel, you may have to double a consonant to protect a short vowel:

fat - fa**ttest**

4. Otherwise, just add the 'est': sick - sick**est**

★ Note that for words like "happ**i**est", ★
the 'i' sounds like a **long 'e'**.

Read the following:

big - bigger - biggest   risky - riskier - riskiest
funny - funnier - funniest   safe - safer - safest
happy - happier - happiest   slow - slower - slowest
lazy - lazier - laziest   strong - stronger - strongest
light - lighter - lightest   sunny - sunniest

Exercise 51.1
Add 'est' to the following words:

1. large   _____

2. lonely   _____

3. rough   _____

4. tough   _____

5. noisy   _____

6. lazy   _____

7. simple   _____

8. heavy   _____

9. strange   _____

10. crazy   _____

craziest
strangest
heaviest
simplest
laziest
noisiest
roughest
loneliest
largest

Lesson 51 - Adding the Suffix 'est'

Exercise 51.2
Read the sentences and write the correct form of the word on the line:

1. That joke was the _____ one I've heard all night!
   funny

2. Flying is one of the _____ ways to travel.
   safe

3. The company _____ your order two days ago.
   ship

4. The teenaged boy is _____ than his friend.
   skinny

5. Abraham Lincoln was one of our _____ presidents.
   great

6. We _____ the luggage through the airport.
   carry

7. Which one of the Great Lakes it the _____?
   large

8. That pear was the _____ fruit I ate.
   juicy

9. The polar bear is _____ than the brown bear.
   big

10. On our vacation, we _____ the mountain.
    climb

11. Her daughter is the _____ one in her class.
    young

funniest, safest, shipped, skinnier, greatest, carried, largest, juiciest, bigger, climbed, youngest

Exercise 51.3
Read each sentence below, and write the missing letter(s) for the incomplete words:

1. We went to the store and ___**ought** food for the party.

2. We all ___**ought** you might like to try something new.

3. Jim ___**ought** his little sister to the museum.

4. In the early 1900's, women ___**ought** for the right to vote.

5. I ___**aught** a cold when watching my sick nephew.

6. The teacher ___**aught** high school math for many years.

bought, thought, brought, fought, caught, taught

Exercise 51.4
Complete the words for the pictures below:

1.   _ _ _ _ _ _

2.   _ _ _ _ _ _ _

3.   _ _ _ _ _

4.   _ _ _ _ _

5.   _ _ _ _ _

6.   _ _ _ _ _ _

7.   _ _ _ _ _

8.   _ _ _ _ _

puzzle, picture, match, apple, table, toilet, bread, straw

Read the following:

technician	dolphin	wrinkle	nervous
physician	sphere	dept	jealous
musician	knock	autumn	hilarious
magician	knee	column	serious
phantom	know	ache	suspicious
pharmacist	knew	echo	infectious
graphic	knowledge	chasm	puncture
prophets	wrist	chemistry	texture
phony	wrong	school	capture
autograph	answer	stomach	assure
elephant	toward	humorous	treasure

Exercise 51.5
Circle the correct word for each sentence:

1. **There / Their / They're** going to search for the treasure.

2. I know that **Jim's / Jims** house is near the soccer field.

3. My dress was **too / to** wrinkly, and needed to be ironed.

4. **There / Their** bird escaped from its cage and flew away.

5. She's **to / too** nervous to answer the question.

6. What type of party **where / were** they planning for Jim?

7. **There / Their** was an echo in the cave.

They're, Jim's, too, Their, too, were, There

Exercise 51.6
Do the dictations for this lesson at www.yourkidcanread.com.

In the lesson for words ending with vowels, we saw that very often, 'i' can sound like a long 'e'. We also see this when the suffixes 'er' and 'est' are added to words ending with a consonant followed by a 'y' (where the 'y' changes to an 'i' that actually sounds like a long 'e'), and, we saw this for words that end with 'ious', such as "curious".

In this lesson, we are going to see more words where 'i' sounds like a long 'e'.

Many of these words have the following endings:

ial = /ee - ul/

ian = /ee - an/

ience = /ee - ens/

ium = /ee - um/

ient = /ee - ent/

Read the following:

material	delirium	Canadian	Columbian
perennial	lithium	historian	experience
proverbial	sodium	librarian	obedience
trinomial	gymnasium	olympian	transient
binomial	sanatarium	ovarian	recipient
memorial	cranium	Iranian	ingredient
stadium	equilibrium	utopian	orient
medium	symposium	vegetarian	ambient
gradient	helium	valedictorian	nutrient

Read the following:

1. The cloth was made from a silk material.
2. Helium is a gas which is lighter than air.
3. James was the recipient of the annual award.
4. We had to take our dog to obedience training.
5. The football team played in the stadium.
6. The babysitter had a lot of experience with children.
7. They played volleyball in the school's gymnasium.
8. Vanilla is an ingredient used in many recipes.

Exercise 52.1
Circle the sounds for the underlined letters:

1.	child	long 'i'	short 'i'
2.	mild	long 'i'	short 'i'
3.	idiot	long 'e'	long 'i'
4.	piano	long 'e'	short 'i'
5.	dismal	long 'e'	short 'i'
6.	drizzle	long 'e'	short 'i'
7.	broccoli	long 'e'	short 'i'
8.	deli	long 'e'	short 'i'
9.	origami	long 'e'	short 'i'
10.	massive	long 'i'	short 'i'
11.	arrive	long 'i'	short 'i'
12.	material	long 'e'	short 'i'

1) long i
2) long i
3) long e
4) long e
5) short i
6) short i
7) long e
8) long e
9) long e
10) short i
11) long i
12) long e

Exercise 52.2

Circle the sound that the letter groups on the left make:

1.	ture	/us/	/shun/	/shuhl/	/chur/	/shur/
2.	tion	/us/	/shun/	/shuhl/	/chur/	/shur/
3.	tial	/us/	/shun/	/shuhl/	/chur/	/shur/
4.	sion	/us/	/shun/	/shuhl/	/chur/	/shur/
5.	cial	/us/	/shun/	/shuhl/	/chur/	/shur/
6.	sure	/us/	/shun/	/shuhl/	/chur/	/shur/
7.	ous	/us/	/shun/	/shuhl/	/chur/	/shur/
8.	oy	/oo/	/oi/	/ou/	long 'o'	long 'i'
9.	ow$_1$	/oo/	/oi/	/ou/	long 'o'	long 'i'
10.	ow$_2$	/oo/	/oi/	/ou/	long 'o'	long 'i'
11.	ew	/oo/	/oi/	/ou/	long 'o'	long 'i'
12.	igh	long 'a'	long 'i'	long 'e'	long 'o'	
13.	eigh	long 'a'	long 'i'	long 'e'	long 'o'	
14.	ay	long 'a'	long 'i'	long 'e'	long 'o'	
15.	oa	long 'a'	long 'i'	long 'e'	long 'o'	
16.	ee	long 'a'	long 'i'	long 'e'	long 'o'	
17.	ea	long 'a'	long 'i'	long 'e'	long 'o'	
18.	aught	/awk/	/aw/	/f/	/oo/	/awt/
19.	ought	/awk/	/aw/	/f/	/oo/	/awt/
20.	alk	/awk/	/aw/	/f/	/oo/	/awt/
21.	ph	/awk/	/aw/	/f/	/oo/	/awt/
22.	au	/awk/	/aw/	/f/	/oo/	/awt/

Exercise 52.3

Write the word that make sense for each sentence:

1. A pirate wears a p__ __ __ __ over his eye.

2. The dancer fell and twisted her a__ __ __ __.

3. For snack we had cheese with cr__ __ __ __ __ __.

4. I bought one t__ __ __ __ __ for the show on Friday.

5. I had to sew the hole in my p__ __ __ __ __.

6. Bill leaned over to c__ __ __ __ the foul ball at the game.

7. I ordered a hot f__ __ __ __ ice-cream sundae.

8. The troll lives under the b__ __ __ __ __.

9. The astronaut was in outer sp__ __ __.

10. He gave the child one more ch__ __ __ __ to be good.

patch, ankle, crackers, ticket, pocket, catch, fudge, bridge, space, chance

Exercise 52.4

Write the word that make sense for each sentence:

1. The short stubby finger on your hand is your __ __ __ __ __.

2. Your leg bends at the __ __ __ __.

3. The season after summer is __ __ __ __ __ __.

4. Land that is surrounded by water is an __ __ __ __ __ __.

5. To cut food, you use a __ __ __ __ __.

thumb, knee, autumn, island, knife

Exercise 52.5

Write the past tense form for each word below. Use the sentence below to help if needed:

Today I _____, but yesterday I _____.

1. catch _____

2. fight _____

3. buy _____

4. shake _____

5. take _____

6. draw _____

7. fly _____

8. make _____

9. ship _____

10. plan _____

11. cry _____

12. worry _____

caught, fought, bought, shook, took, drew, flew, made, shipped, planned, cried, worried

Exercise 52.6

Do the dictations for this lesson at www.yourkidcanread.com.

Common Word Mix-Ups

Some words sound so similar, that many people often mix them up. In an earlier lesson, we discussed homophones (words that sound the same but have different meanings and may be spelled differently). The words below are often the most common word mix ups. If you constantly review the homophones, then you'll know a mix up when you see it, so review that list! In this lesson, we will see some other common words that often get mixed up.

See if you know the differences between the words below.
Circle the word that goes with the meaning:

then / than

This word gets used when comparing something.

it's / its

This word is used for ownership.

lose / loose

Use this word to describe if something is not tight.

chose / choose

This word is the past tense of the *other* word.

who's / whose

This word is used for ownership.

accept / except

This word means to take willingly.

angel / angle

Where two lines meet form an ____.

desert /dessert

This word is for what you eat after dinner.

principal / principle

This word is for the person in charge of a school.

than, its, loose, chose, whose, accept, angle, dessert, principal

Below are the definitions for the words on the previous page:

then / than

then - For ordering events, as in: "I went home and **then** went to bed."
than - This word gets used when comparing something.

it's / its

it's - This is a contraction for "it is".
its - This is for ownership as in: "**Its** wheel came loose."

lose / loose

lose - /looz/ - as in: "Don't **lose** your keys."
loose - /loos/ - as in: "My tooth was **loose**."

chose / choose

chose - the past tense of "choose": "I **chose** the green one."
choose - the present tense of "chose": "I will **choose** the green one."

who's / whose

who's - This is a contraction for "who is".
whose - Used for ownership, as in: "**Whose** house is that?"

accept / except

accept - to take willingly as in: "I **accept** your offer."
except - meaning "other than" as in: "You can all go, **except** the dog."

angel / angle

angel - the 'ge' = /j/. This word depicts a spiritual being with wings.
angle - the 'g' = /g/ as in "get". "Two lines meet to form an **angle**."

desert /dessert

desert - A hot, dry place.
dessert - Something sweet after dinner. Hint: two 's's for two scoops of ice-cream.

principal / principle

principal - The person in charge of a school. Hint: the word "pal" is in this word as in "the princi**pal** is your pal".
principle - A basic truth, good behavior or a rule.

Exercise 53.1
Circle the word that goes with the sentence:

1. I went home and **then / than** went to bed.

2. The dog wagged **it's / its** tail.

3. The heavy woman wanted to **lose / loose** weight.

4. He **chose / choose** to have tuna for lunch.

5. **Who's / Whose** dog is in our yard?

6. **It's / Its** always raining when I go out.

7. What was **there / their** house like?

8. He likes all kinds of food **accept / except** liver.

9. We put an **angel / angle** on top of our Christmas tree.

10. The boy didn't know which toy to **chose / choose** to take.

11. After **loosing / losing** weight, I had to buy new clothes.

12. There is little vegetation in the **desert /dessert**.

13. Their house is larger **than / then** their neighbor's.

14. The road meets the other road at a sharp **angel /angle**.

15. The **principal / principle** called the naughty boy to his office.

16. For **desert / dessert**, I will have the apple pie.

17. Try not to **loose / lose** the game tonight.

18. I didn't know **whose / who's** car was on our driveway.

19. The woman will **accept / except** the invitation to the dinner.

20. **Who's / Whose** going to go with me to the party?

then, its, lose, chose, Whose, It's, their, except, angel, choose, losing, desert, than, angle, principal, dessert, lose, whose, accept, Who's

-273-

Exercise 53.2
Circle the sound that the underlined letters make:

1. loy<u>a</u>l	long 'e'	long 'i'	short 'i'	short 'u'
2. broccol<u>i</u>	long 'e'	long 'i'	short 'i'	short 'u'
3. immed<u>i</u>ate	long 'e'	long 'i'	short 'i'	short 'u'
4. med<u>iu</u>m	long 'e'	long 'i'	short 'i'	short 'u'
5. justif<u>y</u>	long 'e'	long 'i'	short 'i'	short 'u'
6. rectif<u>y</u>	long 'e'	long 'i'	short 'i'	short 'u'
7. satisf<u>y</u>	long 'e'	long 'i'	short 'i'	short 'u'
8. s<u>y</u>stem	long 'e'	long 'i'	short 'i'	short 'u'
9. riv<u>a</u>l	long 'e'	long 'i'	short 'i'	short 'u'
10. m<u>igh</u>t	long 'e'	long 'i'	short 'i'	short 'u'
11. cryst<u>a</u>l	long 'e'	long 'i'	short 'i'	short 'u'
12. or<u>i</u>ent	long 'e'	long 'i'	short 'i'	short 'u'
13 port<u>a</u>l	long 'e'	long 'i'	short 'i'	short 'u'
14. s<u>y</u>mbol	long 'e'	long 'i'	short 'i'	short 'u'
15. tot<u>a</u>l	long 'e'	long 'i'	short 'i'	short 'u'
16. ped<u>a</u>l	long 'e'	long 'i'	short 'i'	short 'u'

1. short u
2. long e
3. long e
4. long i
5. long i
6. long i
7. long i
8. short i
9. short u
10. long i
11. short u
12. long e
13. short i
14. short i
15. short u
16. short u

Exercise 53.3

Circle the word that goes with the sentence:

1. We went **too / to** see the Phantom of the Opera.

2. He had **too / to** many wrong answers.

3. You could **hear / here** an echo across the field.

4. He only took **two / to** classes this semester.

5. We took the highway to get **their / there**.

6. **They're / There** always laughing at something.

7. When we went to the mall, my cousin wanted to go **to / too**.

8. **Where / Were** the animals getting enough exercise?

9. **There / Their** family will be leaving for Europe soon.

10. Try not **too / to** look directly into the sun.

to, too, hear, two, there, They're, too, Were, Their, to

Exercise 53.4

Fill in the blanks with one of the following: **there   their   they're**

1. I love _____ house!

2. The students handed in _____ tests.

3. The girl wasn't allowed to go _____.

4. _____ almost done fixing the roof.

5. I think _____ at the beach.

their, their, there, They're, they're

Exercise 53.5

Do the dictations for this lesson at www.yourkidcanread.com.

Many people have a difficult time with spelling.
To help, we can use a spell checker, an
on-line dictionary or thesaurus,
or memory cues.

When using **spell checkers**, you have to spell the word close enough so the computer has an idea of what you're trying for. Sometimes, with certain words, this can be tricky.

As with spell checkers, you must also spell a word close enough when using an **on-line dictionary**. Often, if this is done, it will offer a few words that it thinks you are searching for. You can then look through the words and find the one you want.

If you have no idea how to spell the word, you can use an on-line (or hard copy) **thesaurus**. Look for a different word that has the same meaning as the word you are trying to spell. The thesaurus will list words that have similar meanings, and then you can look for the word you really want.

Lastly, we can use **memory cues** to help us remember how to spell certain words. We did this when we used the phrase "owls use laundry detergent" to spell the 'ould' in the words: "should", "would" and "could".

Making Memory Cues

1. Make a phrase using the letters inside the word, such as "owls use laundry detergent".

2. Find letters inside a word that make full words, such as 'out' in the word "sh<u>out</u>".

3. Look at the word and see if the shape of the word can help you spell it.

"country"
"country" has the word "count" in it.
Use the phrase below help you remember this:
"You can **count** on your <u>count</u>ry."

"surprise" - in this word you may not remember which
/er/ letter combination to use ('er', 'ir', 'ur').
Make up a phrase to help you remember that it is 'ur':
"You ('u') are ('r') s<u>ur</u>prised."

"ab**ove**" or "gl**ove**"
In both of these words, we have the /uv/ sound
as in the word "l**ove**" (a word that most people know how to spell).

"one"
The word "one" is hiding in the word "al<u>one</u>".
These words are related, since if you are alone,
you are **one** person (by yourself).

"because"
Use the phrase:
"<u>B</u>ig <u>e</u>lephants <u>c</u>an <u>a</u>lways <u>u</u>nderstand <u>s</u>mall <u>e</u>lephants."

"eye"
This word looks like a face, where 'y' is the nose and the
'e's are the eyes.

"hear"
The word "ear" is hiding in this word.
You h<u>ear</u> with your **ear**.

"meat"
The word "eat" is hiding in this word.
Some people **eat** m**eat**.

There are many words that you will need to memorized; the
above are just some examples on creating memory cues.

Other Spelling Tips

- Write the word out and ask yourself if it looks right.

- Say the sounds (not the letter names) as you write.

- Put the spelling of the word to a melody.

- Memorize the *pronunciation* of how the word is spelled. Examples: "mountain" - for the 'ai' say it as a long 'a', even though it's a rule breaker (short 'e'), "water" as /waiter/, etc.

- Practice writing the words many times.

Exercise 54.1

Circle the word that make sense for each sentence:

1. The ball **roled / rolled** down the hill.

2. The car drove down the **road / rode**.

3. Put the garbage in the **waste / waist** basket.

4. The ballet dancer wore a tutu around her **waste / waist**.

5. **Which / Witch** route should we take to get to the museum?

6. What will the **whether / weather** be like tomorrow?

7. Please speak louder, I cannot **here / hear** you.

8. How much do you **way / weigh**?

9. They had to **weight / wait** a long time at the doctor's office.

10. Our company will arrive in an **our / hour**.

rolled, road, waste, waist, Which, weather, hear, weigh, wait, hour

-278-

Exercise 54.2
Write the correct form of the missing word on the line:

1. Eleven inches is _____ than five inches.
   long

2. We _____ on visiting our friend later today.
   plan

3. The frog _____ out of the tank.
   jump

4. The train _____ into the station.
   pull

5. I _____ appreciate your attention to my problem.
   great

6. I _____ did not want to go to the party.
   simple

7. Walking on ice is very _____.
   danger

8. The little girl _____ skipped down the street.
   happy

9. The actor quickly became very _____.
   fame

10. Horror movies are _____ than action movies.
    scary

11. The peacock _____ out its colorful tail.
    fan

longer, planned, pulled, greatly, simply, dangerous, happily, famous, scarier, fanned

Exercise 54.3

Write the correct form of the word on the line:

1. The actress has to _____ her lines.
    memory

2. The _____ day of the week was on Thursday.
    sunny

3. My brother is the _____ person in our family.
    lazy

4. You have to be _____ to get what you need.
    assert

5. The mole on her chin was very _____.
    notice

6. I was very _____ before the test.
    nerve

memorize, sunniest, laziest, assertive, noticeable, nervous

Exercise 54.4

Circle the words that are correctly spelled:

1.	meny / many	7.	office / offiss
2.	people / peeple	8.	notice / notiss
3.	teecher / teacher	9.	animuls / animals
4.	insterment / instrument	10.	stomach / stomack
5.	their / thier	11.	probbly / probably
6.	doctor / docter	12.	favorite / faverit

favorite
probably
stomach
animals
notice
office
doctor
their
instrument
teacher
people
many

Exercise 54.5

Review dictations that were problematic.

Prefixes

In earlier lessons, we saw common suffixes - which are *endings* added to a root word. In this lesson, we are going to see some common **prefixes** - which are letters added at the *beginning* of a word.

 <u>The prefix 're', where the 'e' is *usually* long:</u>

reaffirm	realign	recite	redirect
redo	reapply	recommit	reinstate
reaction	reassure	recount	release

 <u>The prefix 'pre', where the 'e' is *usually* long:</u>

prevent	pretend	preview	preferred
preheat	precede	predict	premature
preclude	pretest	predictably	prepaid

 <u>The prefix 'pro', where the 'o' is *usually* long:</u>

produce	profess	provoke	protract
proceed	profile	prohibit	proclaim
program	progress	prolong	proactive

 <u>The prefix 'un':</u>

undress	unavailable	uncover	undefeated
undo	unable	uncommon	unnerve
unlikely	uncertain	uncomfortable	unearth

A Workbook for Dyslexics - Cheryl Orlassino   -281-

Exercise 55.1

Do the crossword puzzle below. Hint: All of the answers are on the **pre**vious page:

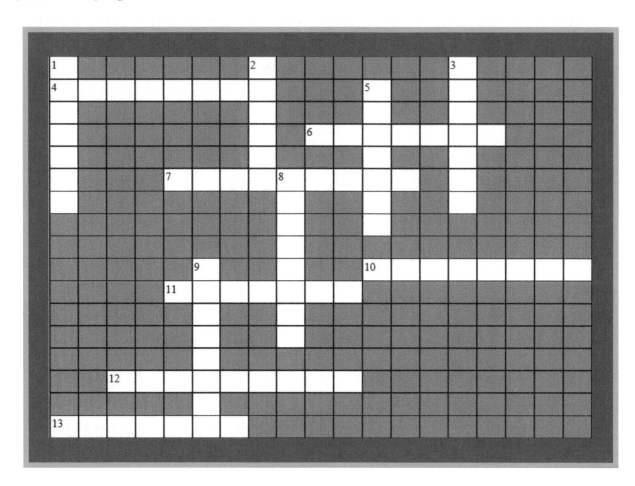

Across

4. He had a bad ___ to the bee sting.
6. To heat an oven before baking.
7. Not certain about something.
10. When something is not likely.
11. The opposite of getting dressed.
12. Before something reached maturity.
13. To have to count over.

Down

1. Do not ___ the snake.
2. Not able to do something.
3. To take out from the earth.
5. To see something ahead of time.
8. To change the direction of something.
9. Not common.

recount
premature
unlikely
uncertain
preheat
reaction

uncommon
redirect
preview
unearth
unable
provoke

Exercise 55.2
Write the **long vowel** sounds that are underlined in the words below:

1.	f<u>ie</u>ld ☐	5.	pr<u>o</u>gram ☐	9.	tax<u>i</u> ☐
2.	<u>eigh</u>t ☐	6.	pod<u>iu</u>m ☐	10.	sod<u>iu</u>m ☐
3.	pr<u>e</u>clude ☐	7.	pl<u>igh</u>t ☐	11.	gr<u>ea</u>t ☐
4.	rel<u>ie</u>f ☐	8.	fr<u>eigh</u>t ☐	12.	gr<u>ee</u>t ☐

Exercise 55.3
Circle the words that you think are spelled correctly:

1.	a lot / a lot	9.	goverment / government
2.	weird / weird	10.	February / Febuary
3.	separate / separate	11.	dissappear / disappear
4.	calander / calendar	12.	column / colum
5.	definitely / definately	13.	twelfth / twelth
6.	fourty / forty	14.	sucsess / success
7.	until / untill	15.	schedule / scedule
8.	library / libery	16.	adress / address

Exercise 55.4
Circle a sound to make a real word for each line below:

1. un____	less	ness	cess	tress
2. ac____	less	ness	cess	tress
3. weight____	less	ness	cess	tress
4. fond____	less	ness	cess	tress
5. mat____	less	ness	cess	tress

Exercise 55.5
Circle the word that makes sense:

1. I'm afraid I might <u>**lose / loose**</u> my diamond earrings again.

2. The girl did not <u>**accept / except**</u> the birthday invitation.

3. We drove across the hot <u>**dessert / desert**</u>.

4. I think <u>**it's / its**</u> funny how he says my name.

5. The basic <u>**principles / principals**</u> for the math class will be covered.

6. A right <u>**angel / angle**</u> is 90 degrees.

7. She is taller <u>**then / than**</u> I am.

8. Julie <u>**chose / choose**</u> the puppy with the spot over his eye.

9. All of the puppies were chosen <u>**accept / except**</u> for the brown one.

10. The dog's collar was too <u>**lose / loose**</u> around his neck.

11. The baby girl is such a sweet <u>**angel / angle**</u>.

12. <u>**Who's / Whose**</u> Halloween costume is hanging in the closet?

13. The scared dog put his tail between <u>**it's / its**</u> legs.

14. For <u>**dessert / desert**</u> we will be having cookies and strawberries.

15. I didn't know which book to <u>**choose / chose**</u> at the library.

16. First we went to the library and <u>**than / then**</u> we went out to eat.

17. <u>**Who's / Whose**</u> going to go to the movie with us?

18. The boy was sent to the <u>**principle's / principal's**</u> office.

lose, accept, desert, it's, principles, angle, than, chose,
except, loose, angel, Whose, its, dessert, choose, then, Who's, principal's

Exercise 55.6
Write the words in their past tense forms.

> Remember, for **one syllable short vowel** words, you must double the consonant to protect the short vowel. In **two syllable short vowel** words, you only double the consonant if the last syllable is <u>stressed</u>.

1. reapply _____
2. pretend _____
3. proceed _____
4. prevent _____
5. happen _____
6. lessen _____
7. fasten _____
8. listen _____
9. excite _____
10. extend _____
11. involve _____
12. program _____
13. undress _____
14. profess _____
15. prolong _____
16. prepare _____

reapplied, pretended, proceeded, prevented, happened, lessened, fastened, listened, excited, extended, involved, programmed, undressed, professed, prolonged, prepared

Exercise 55.7
Review dictations that were problematic.

Letter & Number Reversals

Why do people who have dyslexia reverse letters and/or numbers?

A dyslexic person thinks in very visual terms. When they see a letter or number, they know the shape, but they sometimes don't realize that the direction of the shape matters. For example, a chair is a chair, no matter which way it's facing. It could be upside down, turned one way or another, but it is still a chair. This type of thinking gets applied to letters and numbers.

The most common reversals are:

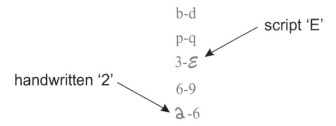

What to do about letter/number reversals?

The main idea is to teach the child that direction *does* matter, and to provide a framework for the child to remember the direction of that letter or number. Here is where you must work with what the child knows (you may have to get creative). Keep an eye out for which letters and/or numbers they are reversing and then come up with a way to teach the proper direction that the child can remember.

On the next page are exercises to combat the common 'b' - 'd' reversal, although, your student may have other reversals as well. Since we are trying to associate the letter direction with the capital letter, you can do this with other letters, but you can't use this technique with numbers. Below are some other strategies for reversals.

1. Have the student draw pictures using the letter or number that they reverse and have him/her identify the visual differences. For example, 6 has a loop on the bottom, while 9 has a loop on the top.

2. Put letter or number refrigerator magnets on the refrigerator (or other metal surface); have the child close their eyes and feel the letter or number and identify it (without moving it around).

3. Form the reversal prone letters or numbers with play dough or clay.

4. Write out the letters or numbers using shaving cream and/or side walk chalk (do this outside). Make them large enough for the child to walk along.

5. Form letters or numbers using string, glue them to cardboard and have the child feel the letter or number and guess what it is (without looking).

Reversal Exercise 1 (only do this exercise if your child reverses d's and b's)
Using colored pencils, have the student write a series of uppercase 'D's across a line in their dictation book:

Now, using a different color, have the student write lowercase 'd's directly on top of the uppercase 'D's (that they just wrote) so that the vertical lines line up:

Ask the student what the letters look like when they are on top of each other. He or she should say that the uppercase 'D' looks like it has a bump sticking out of one side, it takes MORE room. If not, point this out.

Reversal Exercise 2
Repeat the above, but for the letter 'B':

B B B B B

Using a different color, have the student write lowercase 'b's directly on top of the uppercase 'B's so that the vertical lines line up:

B B B B B

Ask the student what the letters look like when they are on top of each other. Here they should notice that lowercase 'b' fits right into uppercase 'B', they don't take up more space (like the 'd's did). If they don't notice this, point it out.

Another method: Draw a box around uppercase 'D' and 'B', then draw lower case 'd' and 'b' as done above and note how 'd' **d**oesn't fit in the box and 'b' does fit in the **b**ox.

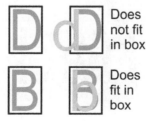

Does not fit in box

Does fit in box

You can also associate the direction the loops are drawn with clockwise and counter-clock wise concepts.

Have your student draw an uppercase 'B' on a white board, and then erase the top curved part to turn it into a lowercase 'b'.

As stated earlier, you can use tactile materials to help your student feel the shape of the letter or number. Use twine, cardboard and glue to create cards. With these, you can play games, such as have the student guess the letter or number without looking. You can also hand them the card (with eyes shut) with the letter/number sideways or upside down and tell the student what the card is and have him/her turn the card so it is correct.

Note that sometimes you only want to do something like this with one letter (or number) that gets reversed, not with both. If the student reverses 'b's and 'd's, then make a "feel board" for only one of the two. This way the 'Bb' will stick in the brain as the one that he or she felt. If you did both letters, you risk confusion.

Lastly, there is the hand method to remember the "b" "d" reversal:

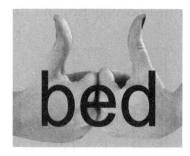

500 Most Commonly Used Words

the	which	made	also
of	their	over	around
and	said	did	another
a	if	down	came
to	do	only	come
in	will	way	work
is	each	find	three
you	about	use	word
that	how	may	must
it	up	water	because
he	out	long	does
for	them	little	part
was	then	very	even
on	she	after	place
are	many	words	well
as	some	called	such
with	so	just	here
his	these	where	take
they	would	most	why
at	other	know	things
be	into	get	help
this	has	through	put
from	more	back	years
I	her	much	different
have	two	before	away
or	like	go	again
by	him	good	off
one	see	new	went
had	time	write	old
not	could	our	number
but	no	used	great
what	make	me	tell
all	than	man	men
were	first	too	say
when	been	any	small
we	its	day	every
there	who	same	found
can	now	right	still
an	people	look	between
your	my	think	name

should	school	night	example
Mr.	important	following	heard
home	until	2 (two)	several
big	1 (one)	picture	change
give	form	being	answer
air	food	study	room
line	keep	second	sea
set	children	eyes	against
own	feet	soon	top
under	land	times	turned
read	side	story	3 (three)
last	without	boys	learn
never	boy	since	point
us	once	white	city
left	animals	days	play
end	life	ever	toward
along	enough	paper	five
while	took	hard	using
might	sometimes	near	himself
next	four	sentence	usually
sound	head	better	money
below	above	best	seen
saw	kind	across	didn't
something	began	during	car
thought	almost	today	morning
both	live	others	given
few	page	however	trees
those	got	sure	I'm
always	earth	means	body
looked	need	knew	upon
show	far	it's	family
large	hand	try	later
often	high	told	turn
together	year	young	move
asked	mother	miles	face
house	light	sun	door
don't	parts	ways	cut
world	country	thing	done
going	father	whole	group
want	let	hear	true

half	though	built	slowly
sentences	started	special	surface
red	idea	ran	river
fish	call	full	numbers
plants	lived	town	common
living	makes	complete	stop
wanted	became	oh	am
black	looking	person	talk
eat	add	hot	quickly
short	become	anything	whether
United States	grow	hold	fine
run	draw	state	build
kinds	yet	list	round
book	hands	stood	dark
gave	less	hundred	girls
order	John	shows	past
open	wind	ten	ball
ground	places	fast	girl
lines	behind	seemed	tried
cold	cannot	felt	road
really	letter	kept	questions
table	among	America	blue
remember	4 (four)	notice	meaning
tree	A	can't	coming
0 (zero)	letters	strong	instead
course	comes	voice	either
front	able	probably	held
known	dog	needed	friends
American	shown	birds	already
space	mean	area	warm
inside	English	horse	taken
ago	rest	Indians	gone
making	perhaps	sounds	finally
Mrs.	certain	matter	summer
early	six	stand	understand
I'll	feel	box	moon
learned	fire	start	animal
brought	ready	that's	mind
close	green	class	outside
nothing	yes	piece	power

says	deep	beautiful	everything
problem	mountains	beginning	game
longer	heavy	moved	system
winter	carefully	everyone	bring
Indian	follow	leave	watch

CPSIA information can be obtained at www.ICGtesting.com
Printed in the USA
BVOW11s2211160115

383599BV00008B/143/P

9 780983 199663